Student Solutions Manual

to accompany Matthew E. Johll's

Investigating Chemistry
Introductory Chemistry from a Forensic Science Perspective
Third Edition

Jason D. Powell

Ferrum College

W. H. Freeman and Company
New York

ISBN-13: 978-1-4641-1294-2

ISBN-10: 1-4641-1294-0

Printed in the United States of America

Second printing

W. H. Freeman and Company
41 Madison Avenue
New York, NY 10010
Houndmills, Basingstoke RG21 6XS England
www.whfreeman.com/chemistry

Table of Contents

Chapter 1

Introduction to Forensic Chemistry

1. According to our chapter, forensic science "draws from multiple sciences—biology, geology, physics, psychology, and especially chemistry."

3. The substances that compose a homogeneous mixture are so evenly distributed that all portions of the mixture are identical. A heterogeneous mixture is not evenly distributed. If the substance has any uneven distribution of its components (i.e., it is "chunky" in some way), then it is a heterogeneous mixture. If its composition is distributed evenly throughout, it is a homogeneous mixture.

5. Pure substances and homogeneous mixtures are both homogeneous, meaning that they both have uniform composition throughout. The method for determining if a sample is a pure substance or a homogeneous mixture depends on the phase (solid, liquid, or gas) of the sample. Generally, the best method is to determine if the substance can be separated into different components by using a physical change. If the sample is a solid, heating the solid to its melting point may determine whether the sample is a pure substance or a mixture. If a portion of the solid melts to liquid and another portion is left behind, then it is a mixture. If the sample is a liquid, boiling it (and then condensing it into another container) will show if the sample is a homogeneous mixture when a solid residue is left after boiling or if the boiling temperature changes as more of the sample boils away. If the sample is a gas, it can be very difficult to determine whether it is a homogeneous mixture or a pure substance. One might try condensing the gas to a liquid, but a better method is gas chromatography (which will be discussed in a later chapter).

7. The type of mixture determines the method used for separating it into its pure components. For example, a solution (homogeneous mixture) composed of salt dissolved in water is best separated by distillation, where the liquid component (water) is evaporated from the mixture and then condensed into another container, leaving the solid component (salt) behind as a residue. A mixture of two solids is more difficult to separate; one might employ the technique of extraction, where one solid is dissolved into a solvent leaving behind the other solid. Other, more complex mixtures will most likely require more involved methods to separate them into their components.

9. Elements are rarely found as pure substances because most elements are reactive under the conditions within Earth's atmosphere, in the oceans, and in the crust. Only elements that are unreactive can be found in their pure form under normal conditions.

11. Some atomic symbols are based on the Latin name for the elements rather than on their contemporary names, often due to historical reasons (and sometimes because a symbol based on the contemporary name was already taken by another element). (E.g., tungsten has the symbol "W" because of its Germanic name, *wolfram* and iron has the symbol "Fe" because of its Latin name, *ferrum.*)

13. It is essential for a scientist to be able to make observations because all branches of science involve testing hypotheses through experimentation. The observations made by a scientist are helpful in providing evidence for or against a particular hypothesis. Without observations, there would be no way of providing support for the validity of a scientific law or theory. Put in the terms of forensic science, observations are required to make a judgment between the guilt or innocence of a suspect (or often to determine whether a crime has taken place at all).

15. The failure to prove a hypothesis is not a failure of the scientific method. Disproving a hypothesis is just as valid a result of the scientific method as is proving a hypothesis; both can require modification or refinement of the hypothesis and further experimental testing.

17. The container shown has a mixture made up of two elements and a compound made from those two elements. The yellow spheres would represent atoms of one element, green spheres would represent atoms of another element, and the compounds would be a yellow sphere connected to a green sphere.

19. (a) gasoline – mixture
    (b) air – mixture
    (c) water – pure substance
    (d) steel – mixture

21. (a) silicon – element
    (b) carbon dioxide – compound (CO_2)
    (c) arsenic – element
    (d) water – compound (H_2O)

23. (a) soil – heterogeneous
    (b) air – homogeneous
    (c) diesel fuel – homogeneous
    (d) concrete – heterogeneous

25. (a) Mg – magnesium   (b) Kr – krypton
    (c) P – phosphorus   (d) Ge – germanium

27. (a) Mn – manganese   (b) Be – beryllium
    (c) Cd – cadmium   (d) Rb – rubidium

29. (a) neon – Ne   (b) zinc – Zn
    (c) rubidium – Rb   (d) iodine – I

31. (a) barium – Ba   (b) cesium – Cs
    (c) silver – Ag   (d) iridium – Ir

33. (a) cadmium = Cd (Ca is the symbol for calcium)
     (b) potassium = K (not potassium = P)
     (c) fluorine = F (not fluorine = Fl)
     (d) zinc = Zn is correct

35. (a) gallium – metal   (b) phosphorus – nonmetal
     (c) boron – metalloid   (d) bismuth – metal

37. (a) As – metal   (b) C – nonmetal
     (c) Ge – metalloid   (d) I – nonmetal

39. (d) $MgSO_4$ contains one magnesium atom, one sulfur atom, and four oxygen atoms

41. (a) 1 calcium atom, 2 fluorine atoms – CaF_2
     (b) 2 sodium atoms, 1 sulfur atom, 4 oxygen atoms – Na_2SO_4
     (c) 2 hydrogen atoms, 1 oxygen atom – H_2O
     (d) 3 magnesium, 2 phosphorus atoms – Mg_3P_2

43. Hematite's formula is Fe_2O_3.

45. (b) Validate the original hypothesis – once a hypothesis has been revised due to the results of experimental testing, it is not necessary to validate the original hypothesis when using the scientific method.

47. (a) In this quotation, Sherlock Holmes is following the scientific method because he is collecting all relevant data before formulating his hypothesis. He is correct in not forming any theories at that stage of his investigation.
     (b) Sherlock is completely correct. Forming a theory is only done after testing a hypothesis that has been formulated and revised as the result of many observations.
     (c) This is not a correct statement. Until a hypothesis or theory has been validated, it is not considered to be correct simply because all other possibilities have been eliminated.

49. Silicon is used to make computer chips. Its melting point is 1687 K (1414°C, 2577°F). Aluminum is frequently used to make electrical connections on computer chips. Its melting point is 933.47 K (660.32°C, 1220.58°F). Based on the fact that the silver metal was melted and the chip was not, the temperature range for the fire was between 933.47 K and 1687 K.

51. The thin-layer chromatography (TLC) results indicate that the evidence may have been methamphetamine ("Meth") because the pink spot for the evidence has the same elution distance as the sample containing pure methamphetamine. However, this is not absolute proof that the person was in possession of the illegal drug. TLC is a screening test and not a confirmatory test for controlled substances; further testing (such as gas chromatography-mass spectrometry, GC-MS) is necessary for proper identification.

Chapter 2

Evidence Collection and Preservation

1. The key difference between chemical changes and physical changes is that in physical changes, the composition does not change. Chemical changes alter the composition of the substance.

3. Physical properties are useful in identifying an unknown substance because they can be measured without altering the chemical identity of the substance, and it is often possible to pinpoint the identity of the substance by using a combination of several different physical properties. When comparing two or more chemical substances, physical properties can often be unique to a specific chemical substance and permit identification.

5. Mass is the amount of substance, measured in grams. Weight is the force of gravity acting on an object, measured in Newtons.

7. The standard SI unit for measuring mass is kilograms (abbreviated kg). The standard unit for measuring distance is meters (abbreviated m).

9. The common metric prefixes listed in the textbook are: Tera – T – 1,000,000,000,000; Giga – G – 1,000,000,000; Mega – M – 1,000,000; kilo – k – 1,000; deci – d – 0.1; centi – c – 0.01; milli – m – 0.001; micro – µ – 0.000 001; nano – n – 0.000 000 001.

11. 2.54 cm = 1 in

13. The accuracy of a measurement is limited by the precision of the measuring instrument if the operator uses only the measurement that is known with a high degree of certainty. By estimating the last digit on a measurement, the operator is including a more precise (and potentially more accurate) value for the measurement.

15. (a) Evaporation of gasoline is a physical change.
    (b) Toasting a marshmallow is a chemical change.
    (c) Filtering a pond water sample is a physical change.
    (d) Burning documents is a chemical change.

17. (a) Hardness is a physical property.
    (b) Corrosiveness is a chemical property.
    (c) Flammability is a chemical property.
    (d) Color is a physical property.

19. (a) Weight depends on gravity.
    (b) Mass is measured in grams.
    (c) Mass measures the amount of matter.
    (d) Weight is measured with a scale.

21. (a) micro-, μ, 0.000 001   (b) kilo-, k, 1,000
     (c) centi-, c, 0.01   (d) nano-, n, 0.000 000 001

23. (a) 0.001 = m (milli-)   (b) 1000 = k (kilo-)
     (c) 0.1 = d (deci-)   (d) 0.000 000 001 = n (nano-)

25. (a) 0.025 g × (1 mg ÷ 0.001 g) = 25 mg
     (b) 3525 mL × (0.001 L ÷ 1 mL) = 3.525 L
     (c) 0.78 m × (1 dm ÷ 0.1 m) = 7.8 dm
     (d) 433 cm × (0.01 cm ÷ 1 m) = 4.33 m

27. (a) 54.0 in × (1 ft ÷ 12 in) = 4.5 ft
     (b) 36.0 ft × (1 yd ÷ 3 ft) = 12.0 yd
     (c) 0.820 m × (1 mm ÷ 0.001 m) = 820 mm = 8.20×10^2 mm
     (d) 9.40 in × (2.54 cm ÷ 1 in) = 23.9 cm

29. (a) 32 ft^2 × (12 in ÷ 1 ft) × (12 in ÷ 1 ft) × (2.54 cm ÷ 1 in) × (2.54 cm ÷ 1 in) × (10^{-2} m ÷ 1 cm) ×
          (10^{-2} m ÷ 1 cm) = 3.0 m^2
          This could be re-written as follows (notice that each conversion must be performed twice
          because the units are squared):
          32 ft^2 × (12 in ÷ 1 ft)^2 × (2.54 cm ÷ 1 in)^2 × (10^{-2} m ÷ 1 cm)^2 = 3.0 m^2
     (b) 49 in^2 × (1 ft ÷ 12 in)^2 = 0.34 ft^2
     (c) 224 cm^3 × (10^{-2} m ÷ 1 cm)^3 × (1 dm ÷ 10^{-1} m)^3 = 0.224 dm^3
     (d) 45 ft^3 × (12 in ÷ 1 ft)^2 × (2.54 cm ÷ 1 in)^3 = 1,300,000 cm^3 = 1.3×10^6 cm^3

31. (a) 554 mm/s × (10^{-3} m ÷ 1 mm) × (1 cm ÷ 10^{-2} m) × (1 in ÷ 2.54 cm) × (1 ft ÷ 12 in)
          × (60 s ÷ 1 min) × (60 min ÷ 1 hr) = 6540 ft/hr = 6.54×10^3 ft/hr
     (b) 73 kg/hr × (10^3 g ÷ 1 kg) × (1 lb ÷ 454 g) × (24 hr ÷ 1 day) = 6.7 lb/day
     (c) 26 km/hr × (10^3 m ÷ 1 km) × (1 cm ÷ 10^{-2} m) × (1 in ÷ 2.54 cm) × (1 ft ÷ 12 in)
          × (1 hr ÷ 60 min) × (1 min ÷ 60 s) = 238 ft/s = 2.4×10^1 ft/s
     (d) 46 mi/gal × (1 km ÷ 0.621 mi) × (1 gal ÷ 3.79 L) = 20. km/L

33. (a) 3007 has 4 significant figures
     (b) 0.00250 has 3 significant figures
     (c) 0.01410 has 4 significant figures
     (d) 3000 has an ambiguous number of significant figures (technically 1 significant figure)

35. (a) 2300 = 2.3×10^3
     (b) 0.0010 = 1.0×10^{-3}
     (c) 17,500 = 1.75×10^4
     (d) 0.0000240 = 2.40×10^{-5}

37. (a) 6.14×10^{-3} = 0.00614
     (b) 2.59×10^5 = 259,000
     (c) 1.0025×10^4 = 10,025
     (d) 2.226×10^{-2} = 0.02226

39. Remember that buret readings are "upside-down"!
     (a) 5.12 mL   (b) 3.55 mL
     (c) 5.70 mL   (d) 2.70 mL

41. (a) 0.0401 contains 3 significant figures
     (b) 1.2×10^3 does not, rewrite as 1.20×10^3
     (c) 0.05 does not, rewrite as 0.0500
     (d) 250.0 does not, rewrite as 250. or 2.50×10^2

43. (a) 35,200 = 3.520×10^4 with 4 significant figures
     (b) 0.008705 = 8.71×10^{-3} with 3 significant figures
     (c) 1,937 = 1.9×10^3 with 2 significant figures
     (d) 0.0219 = 2.2×10^{-2} with 2 significant figures

45. (a) 50.96 = 5.10×10^1 with 3 significant figures
     (b) 78.16 = 7.82×10^1 with 3 significant figures
     (c) 0.3341 = 3.3×10^{-1} with 2 significant figures
     (d) 247.23 = 2.5×10^2 with 2 significant figures

47. (a) $101.34 - 92.1 - 1.793 = 7.447 \approx 7.4$
     (b) $345.3 + 12.12 + 16.10 = 373.52 \approx 373.5$
     (c) $14.5 + 12.34 - 8.991 = 17.849 \approx 17.8$
     (d) $33.9 - 15.60 + 12 = 30.3 \approx 3.0 \times 10^1$

49. (a) $12.2 \div 3.4 \div 0.0127 = 282.5382 \approx 280 = 2.8 \times 10^2$
     (b) $14.9 \div 12.29 \times 0.020 = 0.024247 \approx 0.024$
     (c) $3.0 \times 2.34 \times 329 = 2309.58 \approx 2,300 = 2.3 \times 10^3$
     (d) $76.3 \div 875.023 \times 31.1 = 2.71184 \approx 2.71$

51. (a) $(19.83 \times 2.3) + 4.100 = 45.609 + 4.100 \approx 46 + 4.100 = 50.100 \approx 5.0 \times 10^1$
     (b) $(14.3 - 2.3) \div 2.0 = 12.0 \div 1.2 = 6.0$
     (c) $0.020 \times 211.2 - 40.0 = 4.224 - 40.0 \approx 4.2 - 40.4 = -35.8$
     (d) $12.11 \times (2.8 - 13.3) = 12.11 \times -10.5 \approx 12.11 \times -10.5 = -127.155 \approx -127$

53. Set (c) is the most precise and accurate. The average of the four values is 4.78 and the values vary from a minimum value of 4.68 to a maximum of 4.83. None of the other sets of numbers come this close to the true value of the measurement.

55. In all four cases, use the formula density = mass ÷ volume
     (a) 14.45 g ÷ 10.0 cc = 1.445 g/cc ≈ 1.45 g/cc
     (b) 12.2 g ÷ 3.43 mL = 3.55685... g/mL ≈ 3.56 g/mL
     (c) 9.02 g ÷ 6.23 cm^3 = 1.447833... g/cm^3 ≈ 1.45 g/cm^3
     (d) 7.02 g ÷ 8.29 mL = 0.84680... g/mL ≈ 0.847 g/mL
     (Remember that cc, mL, and cm^3 are all the same unit, so these densities can all be written as g/cm^3 or g/mL or g/cc as you prefer.)

57. In all four cases, use the formula volume = mass ÷ density
     (a) 14.45 g ÷ 0.982 g/mL = 14.7148... mL ≈ 14.7 mL
     (b) 10.0 g ÷ 3.231 g/mL = 3.0950... mL ≈ 3.10 mL
     (c) 4.71 g ÷ 1.34 g/cc = 3.5149... cc ≈ 3.51 cc
     (d) 11.67 g ÷ 2.90 g/cm^3 = 4.0241... cm^3 ≈ 4.02 cm^3

59. In all four cases, use the formula mass = density × volume
    (a) 0.935 g/ml × 23.30 mL = 21.7855 g ≈ 21.8 g
    (b) 1.45 g/cc × 12.22 cc = 17.719 g ≈ 17.7 g
    (c) 13.6 g/mL × 9.32 mL = 126.752 g ≈ 127 g
    (d) 2.25 g/cm^3 × 5.60 cm^3 = 12.6 g ≈ 12.6 g

61. (Determine the nature of the problem.) The investigators believed that Pitera was linked to the mass grave, but they needed evidence to prove that link. (Collect and analyze all relevant data.) The investigators collected soil samples from all over Staten Island for comparison. (Form an educated guess, called a hypothesis, as to what happened.) The hypothesis was that there was a unique soil type at the mass grave and that Pitera would have soil matching that unique type to link him to the crime. (Test the hypothesis.) Bruce Hall examined the color, texture, and composition of the soil in each of the reference samples and in the sample taken from Pitera's shovel. The soil on the shovel matched only the burial site and none of the alibi sites proposed by the defense. This linked Pitera to the crime and helped lead to a conviction in the case.

63. Soil on the blade of a shovel is easily brushed off or mixed with other soils as the shovel is used repeatedly. The soil in the rounded-over flange of the shovel has been compacted and doesn't mix with soil as the shovel is used at new sites.

65. volume = mass ÷ density
    1.00 pound × (453.5 g ÷ 1 pound) = 453.5 g ≈ 454 g DDNP
    volume = 454 g ÷ 1.63 g/mL = 278.5276... mL ≈ 279 mL

67. 15 mg/(dL·hr) × 0.001 g ÷ 1 mg = 0.015 g/(dL·hr)
    0.015 g/(dL·hr) × 1 hr ÷ 60 min = 0.00025 g/(dL·min)

69. 17.84 g × 1 mL ÷ 2.64 g = 6.76 mL
    6.76 mL + 30.00 mL = 36.76 mL

71. If a suspected arson sample sent to the laboratory comes back negative, that means that accelerants were not found in the sample. This means that the accelerants were not detected, not that they weren't used nor that the fire wasn't deliberately set. If a sample comes back positive for petroleum-based accelerants, that means that accelerants were present in the fire. It could mean that the fire was deliberately set or it could mean that the fire burned in a location that already contained accelerants (such as a garage or storage shed). The investigator can determine only if accelerants were detected in the arson sample. How that information is used in the investigation will depend on the location and type of fire and the suspects being considered.

73. If a glass sample has a softening point in the range of 819°C to 833°C, the possible glass types are borosilicate (Pyrex®) and potash borosilicate. Once the density is determined to be 2.23 g/cm^3, the glass sample is positively identified as being borosilicate (Pyrex®).

75. 1000 ft/s × (12 in ÷ 1 ft) × (2.54 cm ÷ 1 in) × (10^{-2} m ÷ 1 cm) = 304.8 m/s ≈ 300 m/s
    15 s × 300 m/s = 4500 m ≈ 5×10^3 m traveled in the first 15 s after being fired

77. According to question 76, 13.4 g caffeine or 0.0210 g nicotine would be lethal to 50% of the human population.

0.0210 g nicotine × (1 mg ÷ 10^{-3} g) × (1 cigarette ÷ 1.89 mg nicotine) = 11.1 cigarettes

13.4 g caffeine × (1 mg ÷ 10^{-3} g) × (1 oz ÷ 9.76 mg caffeine) × (1 can Red Bull ÷ 8.2 oz) = 167 cans of Red Bull

79.

Solution 4 (25 mL, 1.80 g/mL) floats on top
Mineral 4 (2.16 g/mL) floats at the interface of Solutions 2 and 4
Solution 2 (25 mL, 2.45 g/mL)
Mineral 1 (2.58 g/mL) floats at the interface of Solutions 3 and 2
Solution 3 (50 mL, 3.34 g/mL)
Mineral 2 (3.56 g/mL) floats at the interface of solutions 1 and 3
Solution 1 (50 mL, 4.25 g/mL)
Mineral 3 (4.35 g/mL) sinks to the bottom

81. It was not reasonable to convict the suspect based on the evidence given. The scientific method was only applied to the second case.

83. 2.236 g × (1 grain ÷ 0.0648 g) = 34.5 grains

The brass casing measures 5.7 mm diameter × 15.0 mm length

The recovered bullet and case are consistent with the .22LR (5.7 mm × 15.0 mm, 30–60 grains) and not the .25 auto (6.4 mm × 16.0 mm, 35–50 grains).

Chapter 3

Atomic Clues

1. Atoms were described by Leucippus and Democritus as small, hard, indivisible particles that come in various sizes, shapes, and weights. They were thought to be in constant motion and to combine to make up all the various forms of matter. The observable properties of matter were thought to be a direct result of the type of atoms it contained.

3. Aristotle believed that matter could be divided infinitely (a direct contradiction of the theory proposed by the atomists).

5. The law of conservation of mass says that matter changes form and is neither created nor destroyed in a chemical reaction.

7. While many of his contemporaries were making careful measurements of mass, the difference in Lavoisier's experiments was that he was using closed systems. By making careful measurements of the mass of a closed system, Lavoisier was able to demonstrate the law of conservation of mass.

9. The law of definite proportions (law of constant composition) helped scientists understand that atoms of different elements can combine in specific ratios to make different compounds. It is not just the identity of the elements that matters.

11. In science, a theory is the best current explanation of a phenomenon. In popular use, it is often expressed as an opinion that can be easily swayed by argument.

13. The four principles of Dalton's Atomic Theory: 1. All matter is made up of tiny, indivisible particles called atoms; 2. Atoms cannot be created, destroyed, or transformed into other atoms in a chemical reaction; 3. All atoms of a given element are identical; 4. Atoms combine in simple, whole-number ratios to form compounds.

15. The law of definite proportions is a restatement of the fourth principle of Dalton's atomic theory: atoms combine in simple, whole-number ratios to form compounds.

17. We will represent carbon atoms as black circles and oxygen atoms as white circles:

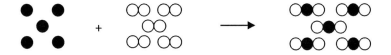

This obeys the law of conservation of mass because it has the same number of carbon atoms on the reagent side as it does on the product side (5) and the same number of oxygen atoms on the reagent side as it does on the product side (10).

19.   The law of multiple proportions shows that different ratios of the same elements yield different compounds. One carbon and one oxygen atom bonded together makes carbon monoxide, while one carbon atom bonded to two oxygen atoms makes carbon dioxide.

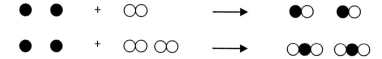

21.   There are actually more than three subatomic particles, but these three are the most important subatomic particles from the perspective of chemistry: electrons, protons, and neutrons.

23.   Rutherford compared his results to seeing an artillery shell reflected back by having it hit a piece of paper. He called the dense positive region in the gold foil the nucleus and subsequently explored the structure of the atom by other techniques to arrive at a physical model to account for the observed behavior.

25.   Isotopes of the same element are different because they have a different mass per atom. This difference in mass results from a differing number of neutrons in the nucleus. (If the atoms had differing numbers of protons in the nucleus, they wouldn't be the same element. If they had differing numbers of electrons, they would be ions with different overall charges.)

27.   The atomic mass for einsteinium (Es) is listed as (252) because the isotope ^{252}Es is the longest-lived isotope of the element. The isotopes of einsteinium have short half-lives that make it impossible to measure an accurate average atomic mass for the element.

29.   A continuous spectrum is produced by a source that produces a large number of emissions at varying wavelengths. A good example is an incandescent light bulb, where the high temperature of the tungsten filament causes the emission of light at wavelengths throughout the visible spectrum. A line spectrum is produced by a source that is based on atomic emission from a single element. High voltage discharge tubes containing samples of elements in the gas phase produce such a spectrum, as do flame emissions of many inorganic salts.

31.   The line spectrum from an excited lithium atom results from electronic transitions of the three electrons within the atomic orbitals of the lithium atom. The line spectrum from an excited cesium atom results from electronic transitions of the 55 electrons within the atomic orbitals of the cesium atom. The higher number of electrons results in a more complex line spectrum.

33.   Radio waves have the longest wavelength and gamma rays have the shortest wavelength of the forms of electromagnetic radiation.

35.   As the wavelength of light increases, the energy decreases. As the wavelength of light decreases, the energy increases. (Energy and wavelength are inversely proportional.)

37.   According to the Heisenberg Uncertainty Principle, if the location of an electron is known precisely, then at that instant the energy cannot be known precisely, and vice versa.

39. An *s*-orbital is a sphere centered at the nucleus of the atom. A *p*-orbital has two spherical lobes (similar to a peanut or dumbbell) with the two lobes meeting at the nucleus of the atom. The figures below are taken from Figures 3.16b (*s*-orbital) and 3.17b (*p*-orbitals).

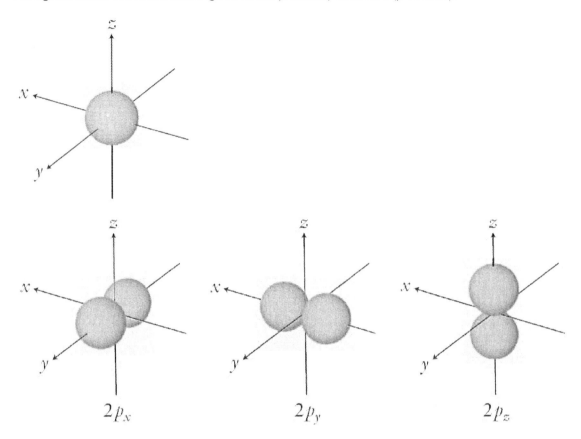

41. The order is: Democritus (440 B.C.), Lavoisier (1785), Dalton (1803), and Thomson (1897).

43. (c) The chemical reactions could exchange mass with the surroundings. This is false because the reaction vessel was a closed system. By definition, a closed system cannot exchange any matter with its surroundings.

45. In all cases, the total mass of reactants should be equal to the total mass of products (and leftover reactants, if the reaction does not go to completion).   The missing quantity is determined by difference.
(a) 13.5 g water + 33.0 g carbon dioxide → <u>46.5</u> g carbonic acid
(b) <u>60.0</u> g sodium hydroxide + 30.0 g hydrofluoric acid → 27.0 g water + 63.0 g sodium fluoride
(c) 50.0 g calcium carbonate + 40.0 g sodium hydroxide → 53.0 g sodium carbonate + <u>37.0</u> g calcium hydroxide
(d) 8.0 g sodium hydroxide + <u>8.8</u> g carbon dioxide → 16.8 g sodium hydrogen carbonate

47. The observation that the vast majority of alpha particles passed directly through the gold foil leads to the conclusion that:
    (b) The majority of the atom must consist of empty space.
    By extension, it is reasonable to conclude that:
    (a) The positive region of the atom had to be small.
    (d) The positive region of the atom is very dense.
    These are not conclusions made directly from the observation mentioned, but they are consistent with the observation and so are still true. The only conclusion from the list that is incorrect is:
    (c) The alpha particle made a direct hit on the positive region.

49. The information required to answer this question is found in Table 1.

Particle	Charge	Mass (amu)	Symbol
electron	−1	0.0005486	e^-
proton	+1	1.0073	p or p^+ or H^+
neutron	0	1.0087	n or n^0

51. Remember that the atomic symbol is determined by the atomic number (Z), which is equal to the number of protons. For a neutral atom, the number of electrons must equal the number of protons. The mass number (the superscript value) must be equal to the sum of the number of protons and the number of neutrons.

Protons	Neutrons	Electrons	Isotope symbol
28	30	28	$^{58}_{28}\text{Ni}$
22	25	22	$^{47}_{22}\text{Ti}$
6	6	6	^{12}C
18	20	18	$^{38}_{18}\text{Ar}$

53. (a) Z = 12, neutrons = 12: $^{24}_{12}\text{Mg}$
    (b) Z = 19, neutrons = 22: $^{41}_{19}\text{K}$
    (c) Z = 34, neutrons = 40: $^{74}_{34}\text{Se}$
    (d) Z = 56, neutrons = 80: $^{136}_{56}\text{Ba}$

55. The atomic mass of magnesium on the periodic table is 24.3050. Therefore, the ^{24}Mg isotope is probably the most abundant. Option (a) is the correct answer.

57. B: (10.013 amu × 0.199) + (11.009 amu × 0.801) = 10.811 amu
    Br: (78.918 amu × 0.5069) + (80.916 amu × 0.4931) = 79.903 amu
    Rb: (84.912 amu × 0.7217) + (86.909 amu × 0.2783) = 85.468 amu
    Sb: (120.904 amu × 0.5721) + (122.904 amu × 0.4279) = 121.760 amu

59. (b) Electrons are stable in excited states. This is a false statement about the production of line spectra because the line spectrum is produced by the emission of energy as the electrons in excited states decay back to the ground state.

61. (a) $v = 3.00 \times 10^8$ m/s $\div 425.0 \times 10^{-9}$ m $= 1.224 \times 10^{15}$ Hz
    (b) $v = 3.00 \times 10^8$ m/s $\div 682.0 \times 10^{-9}$ m $= 4.399 \times 10^{14}$ Hz
    (c) $v = 3.00 \times 10^8$ m/s $\div 850.0 \times 10^{-9}$ m $= 3.529 \times 10^{14}$ Hz
    (d) $v = 3.00 \times 10^8$ m/s $\div 282.0 \times 10^{-9}$ m $= 1.064 \times 10^{15}$ Hz

63. (a) $\lambda = 3.00 \times 10^8$ m/s $\div 2.35 \times 10^{15}$ Hz $= 1.28 \times 10^{-7}$ m $= 128$ nm
    (b) $\lambda = 3.00 \times 10^8$ m/s $\div 5.68 \times 10^{15}$ Hz $= 5.28 \times 10^{-8}$ m $= 52.8$ nm
    (c) $\lambda = 3.00 \times 10^8$ m/s $\div 8.41 \times 10^{15}$ Hz $= 3.57 \times 10^{-8}$ m $= 35.7$ nm
    (d) $\lambda = 3.00 \times 10^8$ m/s $\div 3.03 \times 10^{15}$ Hz $= 9.90 \times 10^{-8}$ m $= 99.0$ nm

65. Using data from problem 61:
    (a) $E = h\,v = 6.626 \times 10^{-34}$ J s $\times 1.224 \times 10^{15}$ Hz $= 4.677 \times 10^{-19}$ J
    (b) $E = h\,v = 6.626 \times 10^{-34}$ J s $\times 4.399 \times 10^{14}$ Hz $= 2.915 \times 10^{-19}$ J
    (c) $E = h\,v = 6.626 \times 10^{-34}$ J s $\times 3.529 \times 10^{14}$ Hz $= 2.339 \times 10^{-19}$ J
    (d) $E = h\,v = 6.626 \times 10^{-34}$ J s $\times 1.064 \times 10^{15}$ Hz $= 7.049 \times 10^{-19}$ J

67. Using data from problem 63:
    (a) $E = h\,v = 6.626 \times 10^{-34}$ J s $\times 2.35 \times 10^{15}$ Hz $= 1.56 \times 10^{-18}$ J
    (b) $E = h\,v = 6.626 \times 10^{-34}$ J s $\times 5.68 \times 10^{15}$ Hz $= 3.76 \times 10^{-18}$ J
    (c) $E = h\,v = 6.626 \times 10^{-34}$ J s $\times 8.41 \times 10^{15}$ Hz $= 5.57 \times 10^{-18}$ J
    (d) $E = h\,v = 6.626 \times 10^{-34}$ J s $\times 3.03 \times 10^{15}$ Hz $= 2.01 \times 10^{-18}$ J

69. (a) Ni: $1s^2 2s^2 2p^6 3s^2 3p^6 4s^2 3d^8$
    (b) O: $1s^2 2s^2 2p^4$
    (c) Cl: $1s^2 2s^2 2p^6 3s^2 3p^5$
    (d) Mn: $1s^2 2s^2 2p^6 3s^2 3p^6 4s^2 3d^5$

71. (a) C: $[\text{He}]2s^2 2p^2$
    (b) Ge: $[\text{Ar}]4s^2 3d^{10} 4p^2$
    (c) Sb: $[\text{Kr}]5s^2 4d^{10} 5p^3$
    (d) As: $[\text{Ar}]4s^2 3d^{10} 4p^3$

73. (a) $1s^2 2s^2 2p^6 3s^2 3p^6 4s^2 3d^{10} 4p^6 5s^2 4d^7$ = Rh
    (b) $1s^2 2s^2 2p^6 3s^2 3p^3$ = P
    (c) $1s^2 2s^2 2p^6 3s^2 3p^6 4s^2 3d^{10} 4p^6 5s^2$ = Sr
    (d) $1s^2 2s^2 2p^6 3s^2 3p^6 4s^2 3d^3$ = V

75. (a) $[\text{Ne}]3s^2 3p^3$ = P
    (b) $[\text{Kr}]5s^2 4d^{10} 5p^4$ = Te
    (c) $[\text{Ne}]3s^1$ = Na
    (d) $[\text{Kr}]5s^2 4d^{10} 5p^5$ = I

77. (a) Y: $[\text{Kr}]5s^2 4d^1$ – The error is in the noble gas core: Kr not Ar
    (b) Sc: $[\text{Ar}]4s^2 3d^1$ – The error is in the principal quantum number for the d orbitals: 3d not 4d
    (c) Fe: $1s^2 2s^2 2p^6 3s^2 3p^6 4s^2 3d^6$ – The principal quantum numbers do not go up for every orbital
    (d) F: $1s^2\, 2s^2\, 2p^5$ – Fluorine only has 5 electrons in its 2p orbital

79. All isotopes of strontium have 38 protons (because the number of protons is equal to Z, the atomic number of the element) and electrons (if the atom is neutral, the number of electrons equals the number of protons). The number of neutrons is equal to the mass number minus the atomic number.

    ^{88}Sr: 38 protons, 50 neutrons, 38 electrons
    ^{87}Sr: 38 protons, 49 neutrons, 38 electrons
    ^{86}Sr: 38 protons, 48 neutrons, 38 electrons
    ^{84}Sr: 38 protons, 46 neutrons, 38 electrons

81. Blue: 447 nm
    $v = 3.00 \times 10^8$ m/s / 447×10^{-9} m $= 6.71 \times 10^{14}$ Hz
    $E = (6.626 \times 10^{-34}$ Js$) \times (6.71 \times 10^{14}$ Hz$) = 4.45 \times 10^{-19}$ J
    Green: 502 nm
    $v = 3.00 \times 10^8$ m/s / 502×10^{-9} m $= 5.96 \times 10^{14}$ Hz
    $E = (6.626 \times 10^{-34}$ Js$) \times (5.96 \times 10^{14}$ Hz$) = 3.95 \times 10^{-19}$ J
    Yellow: 597 nm
    $v = 3.00 \times 10^8$ m/s / 597×10^{-9} m $= 5.02 \times 10^{14}$ Hz
    $E = (6.626 \times 10^{-34}$ Js$) \times (5.02 \times 10^{14}$ Hz$) = 3.33 \times 10^{-19}$ J
    Red: 668 nm
    $v = 3.00 \times 10^8$ m/s / 668×10^{-9} m $= 4.49 \times 10^{14}$ Hz
    $E = (6.626 \times 10^{-34}$ Js$) \times (4.49 \times 10^{14}$ Hz$) = 2.98 \times 10^{-19}$ J

83. Thallium-203 contains 81 protons, 81 electrons, and 122 neutrons
    Thallium-205 contains 81 protons, 81 electrons, and 124 neutrons.

85. If $\lambda = 223.1$ nm $= 2.231 \times 10^{-7}$ m, then
    $v = c / \lambda = 3.00 \times 108$ m/s / 2.231×10^{-7} m $= 1.34 \times 10^{15}$ Hz, and
    $E = hv = (6.626 \times 10^{-34}$ Js$) \times (1.344 \times 10^{15}$ Hz$) = 8.91 \times 10^{-19}$J

87. 254 nm:
    $v = 3.00 \times 10^8$ m/s / 254×10^{-9} m $= 1.18 \times 10^{15}$ Hz
    $E = (6.626 \times 10^{-34}$ Js$) \times (1.18 \times 10^{15}$ Hz$) = 7.82 \times 10^{-19}$ J
    7.82×10^{-19} J $\times$ (1 kJ / 10^3 J) $\times$ (6.022×10^{23} /mol) $= 472$ kJ/mol
    395 nm:
    $v = 3.00 \times 10^8$ m/s / 395×10^{-9} m $= 7.59 \times 10^{14}$ Hz
    $E = (6.626 \times 10^{-34}$ Js$) \times (7.59 \times 10^{14}$ Hz$) = 5.02 \times 10^{-19}$ J
    5.02×10^{-19} J $\times$ (1 kJ / 10^3 J) $\times$ (6.022×10^{23} /mol) $= 303$ kJ/mol

    The shorter wavelength ultraviolet light has enough energy to break the 413 kJ/mol carbon-hydrogen bond. The longer wavelength ultraviolet light does not.

89. The match between the evidence recovered from the burn victim and the elemental profile of the explosives used by the neighbors is compelling evidence, but it alone does not prove the neighbors guilty. It is still possible that someone else might have used another lot of the same batch of explosives (with the same elemental profile). They may even have stolen some of the neighbors' explosives and used them, or perhaps the victim had stolen some of the neighbors' and accidentally been killed.

91.   Because stable isotope ratios are different in different regions of Earth, stable isotope analysis of cocaine samples should show a correlation between the stable isotope ratios of the cocaine sample and the corresponding geographic region. By comparing the seized samples with known samples, the region of origin can be determined.

Chapter 4

Chemical Evidence

1. The periodic table is printed inside the cover of your textbook. Here is a smaller version with the appropriate sections labeled:

Periodic Table of the Elements

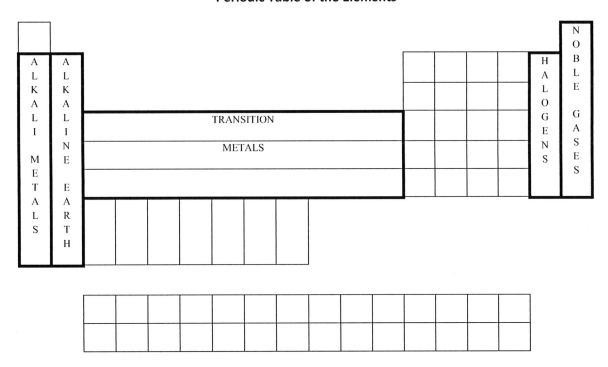

3. Metals tend to form cations (they tend to lose electrons, which leaves them with a positive charge); they are located on the left-hand side of the periodic table. Nonmetals tend to form anions (they tend to gain electrons, which leaves them with a negative charge); they are located on the right-hand side of the periodic table.

5. Covalent bonds typically form between nonmetallic elements.

7. Cations are formed when an atom loses one or more electrons. Anions are formed when an atom gains one or more electrons.

9. Polyatomic ions are ions composed of more than one atom bonded together. Examples include NH_4^+, NO_3^-, SO_4^{2-}, PO_4^{3-}, and $CH_3CO_2^-$.

11. In MgS, there are Mg^{2+} cations and S^{2-} anions. In NaF, there are Na^+ cations and F^- anions. The divalent ions (Mg^{2+} and S^{2-}) have stronger electrostatic attraction than do the monovalent ions (Na^+ and F^-).

13. Balanced chemical equations are important because they reflect the fact that all chemical reactions obey the law of conservation of mass. Since matter is neither created nor destroyed in a chemical reaction, the chemical equation should be balanced to reflect that fact.

15. The concept of the mole is necessary to make a connection between the world that we operate in and the abstract world of atoms. Without it, scientists would be unable to relate the mass of a substance with the number of atoms present in the substance.

17. The limiting reactant is the one that determines the maximum theoretical amount of product formed. If the limiting reactant is unknown, it is impossible to predict how much product is formed as a result of a chemical reaction.

19. A solution containing a greater amount of red dye #40 is more concentrated than a solution containing a lower amount of the dye. The more concentrated solution contains more dye molecules in the same volume of solution. The higher the concentration of a colored compound, the less light passes through the solution, and the solution appears darker.

21. The halogens are F, Cl, Br, I, and At.
    (a) I   (b) Br
    (c) F   (d) Cl

23. Group number is the number of the column, and period number is the number of the row where an element resides.
    (a) K: group 1, alkali metal, period 4
    (b) Ru: group 8, transition metal, period 5
    (c) Ne: group 18, noble gas, period 2
    (d) As: group 15, pnictogen, period 4

25. (a) Period 6, group 10: platinum, Pt
    (b) Halogen, period 2: fluorine, F
    (c) Noble gas, period 4: krypton, Kr
    (d) Period 4, group 14: arsenic, As

27. (a) BF_3: boron trifluoride
    (b) SF_6: sulfur hexafluoride
    (c) CF_4: carbon tetrafluoride
    (d) CS_2: carbon disulfide

29. (a) Disulfur dichloride: S_2Cl_2
    (b) Dinitrogen pentasulfide: N_2S_5
    (c) Sulfur tetrafluoride: SF_4
    (d) Sulfur trioxide: SO_3

31.   The charge on an ion can be predicted (in general) by the charge that makes the element have the same electron configuration as the nearest noble gas. Transition metals are notable exceptions to this.
      (a) K: +1   (b) N: −3 (also +5)
      (c) Pb: +2, +4   (d) Br: −1

33.   The formula of the ionic compound depends on the charges of the ions. The overall charge on the compound must be neutral, so the total positive charge provided by the cation must cancel the total negative charge provided by the anion.
      (a) Al^{3+}, Cl^-: $AlCl_3$ (b) Cs^+, F^-: CsF
      (c) Cd^{2+}, O^{2-}: CdO (d) Sr^{2+}, I^-: SrI_2

35.   (a) Nitrate ion: NO_3^-, −1
      (b) Hydroxide ion: OH^-, −1
      (c) Cyanide ion: CN^-, -1
      (d) Phosphate ion: PO_4^{3-}, −3

37.   The formula of the ionic compound depends on the charges of the ions. The overall charge on the compound must be neutral, so the total positive charge provided by the cation must cancel the total negative charge provided by the anion.
      (a) Cesium acetate: $Cs^+ + C_2H_3O_2^- = CsC_2H_3O_2$
      (b) Potassium carbonate: $K^+ + CO_3^{2-} = K_2CO_3$
      (c) Barium phosphate: $Ba^{2+} + PO_4^{3-} = Ba_3(PO_4)_2$
      (d) Aluminum permanganate: $Al^{3+} + MnO_4^- = Al(MnO_4)_3$

39.   The charge of the cation must be such that the total positive charge provided by the cation must cancel the total negative charge provided by the anion to make a neutral ionic compound.
      (a) $CuCl_2$: Since Cl^- (chloride) has a −1 charge, the Cu must be +2
      (b) $Co(NO_3)_2$: Since NO_3^- (nitrate) has a −1 charge, the Co must be +2
      (c) $CuCl$: Since Cl^- (chloride) has a −1 charge, the Cu must be +1
      (d) CrO: Since O^{2-} (oxide) has a −2 charge, the Cr must be +2

41.   (a) Al_2S_3: aluminum sulfide
      (b) MgO: magnesium oxide
      (c) KOH: potassium hydroxide
      (d) $AlPO_4$: aluminum phosphate

43.   For monatomic ions that can have multiple charges (like the transition metal cations), it is common to include the charge (later called the oxidation state) of the ion as a roman numeral after the name of the element.
      (a) $CuCl_2$: copper(II) chloride
      (b) $Co(NO_3)_2$: cobalt(II) nitrate
      (c) $CuCl$: copper(I) chloride
      (d) CrO: chromium(II) oxide

45.   The important step is to get the correct formula for each compound. Remember that the net charge on an ionic compound should be zero, so the total positive charge provided by the cation must cancel the total negative charge provided by the anion.
      $3 NaCN + Fe(NO_3)_3 \rightarrow Fe(CN)_3 + 3 NaNO_3$

47. To balance, check to see which elements are not balanced in the equation as written and adjust the coefficients on the compounds to balance those elements one at a time. Sometimes it is easier to consider polyatomic ions as a single unit rather than the individual elements within the ion.

(a) $BaCl_2 + Na_3PO_4 \rightarrow Ba_3(PO_4)_2 + NaCl$ all elements unbalanced
     $3 BaCl_2 + Na_3PO_4 \rightarrow Ba_3(PO_4)_2 + NaCl$ Ba balanced
     $3 BaCl_2 + 2 Na_3PO_4 \rightarrow Ba_3(PO_4)_2 + NaCl$ Ba, PO_4 balanced
     $3 BaCl_2 + 2 Na_3PO_4 \rightarrow Ba_3(PO_4)_2 + 6 NaCl$ all elements balanced

(b) $Na_2S + Fe(NO_3)_2 \rightarrow NaNO_3 + FeS$ Fe, S balanced
     $Na_2S + Fe(NO_3)_2 \rightarrow 2 NaNO_3 + FeS$ all elements balanced

(c) $C_3H_8 + O_2 \rightarrow CO_2 + H_2O$ all elements unbalanced

(For combustion reactions, it is usually helpful to balance first carbon, then hydrogen, and finally oxygen. If you practice enough of these sorts of problems, you will see why.)

$C_3H_8 + O_2 \rightarrow 3 CO_2 + H_2O$ C balanced
$C_3H_8 + O_2 \rightarrow 3 CO_2 + 4 H_2O$ C,   H balanced
$C_3H_8 + 5 O_2 \rightarrow 3 CO_2 + 4 H_2O$ all elements balanced

(d) $Ca(C_2H_3O_2)_2 + KOH \rightarrow KC_2H_3O_2 + Ca(OH)_2$ K, Ca balanced

(Sometimes it is easy to see that two compounds need to have the same coefficient. In this case, balancing the acetate ion, $C_2H_3O_2^-$, requires a coefficient of 2 on $K_2C_2H_3O_2$. This would unbalance K, so putting a coefficient of 2 on KOH at the same time avoids that unbalance. Coincidentally, this completely balances the equation.)

$Ca(C_2H_3O_2)_2 + 2 KOH \rightarrow 2 KC_2H_3O_2 + Ca(OH)_2$ all elements balanced

49. (a) The products will be ammonium acetate and silver bromide
     $NH_4Br + AgC_2H_3O_2 \rightarrow NH_4C_2H_3O_2 + AgBr$
(b) The products will be potassium nitrate and lead(II) sulfate
     $K_2SO_4 + Pb(NO_3)_2 \rightarrow 2 KNO_3 + PbSO_4$
(c) The products will be sodium chloride and magnesium phosphate
     $2 Na_3PO_4 + 3 MgCl_2 \rightarrow 6 NaCl + Mg_3(PO_4)_2$
(d) The products will be lithium sulfate and copper(I) carbonate
     $Li_2CO_3 + Cu_2SO_4 \rightarrow Li_2SO_4 + Cu_2CO_3$

51. (a) $CsC_2H_3O_2$: $132.905 + 2(12.011) + 3(1.0079) + 2(15.999) = 191.956$ g/mol
(b) K_2CO_3: $2(39.098) + 12.011 + 3(15.999) = 138.206$ g/mol
(c) $Ba_3(PO_4)_2$: $3(137.327) + 2(30.974) + 8(15.999) = 601.933$ g/mol
(d) $Al(MnO_4)_3$: $26.982 + 3(54.938) + 12(15.999) = 383.789$ g/mol

53. (a) 21.0 g $AgNO_3$ ÷ (107.8682 g/mol Ag + 14.00674 g/mol N + 3 × (15.9994 g/mol O))
        = 0.123 mol $AgNO_3$
    (b) 0.295 g C_3H_8 ÷ (3 × (12.0115 g/mol C) + 8 × (1.00794 g/mol H)) = 0.00669 mol C_3H_8
    (c) 25.0 g $Fe(NO_3)_2$ ÷ (55.845 g/mol Fe + 2 × (14.00674 g/mol N) + 6 × (15.9994 g/mol O))
        = 0.139 mol $Fe(NO_3)_2$
    (d) 4.10 g CO_2 ÷ (12.0115 g/mol C + 2 × (15.9994 g/mol O)) ≈ 0.0932 mol CO_2

55. (a) 1.50 mol N_2O_3 × (2 × (14.0067 g/mol N) + 3 × (15.9994 g/mol O)) = 114 g N_2O_3
    (b) 0.375 mol Cl_2 × (2 × (35.453 g/mol Cl)) = 26.6 g Cl_2
    (c) 2.25 mol FeO × (55.845 g/mol Fe + 15.9994 g/mol O) = 162 g FeO
    (d) 1.33 mol $NH_4C_2H_3O_2$ × (14.0067 g/mol N + 7 × (1.00794 g/mol H) + 2 × (12.0115 g/mol C) +
        2 × (15.9994 g/mol O)) = 103 g $NH_4C_2H_3O_2$

57.   When doing calculations that involve a chemical reaction, remember to always work in moles, not grams. The chemical equation describes the relationships between moles of substance, not mass of substance.

       27.8 g $BaCl_2$ ÷ (137.327 g/mol Ba + 2 × (35.453 g/mol Cl)) = 0.134 mol $BaCl_2$
       0.134 mol $BaCl_2$ × (1 mol $BaSO_4$ / 1 mol $BaCl_2$) = 134 mol $BaSO_4$
       0.134 mol $BaSO_4$ × (137.327 g/mol Ba + 32.066 g/mol S + 4 × (15.9994 g/mol O))
       = 31.2 g $BaSO_4$ produced

59.   40.5 g $BaCl_2$ ÷ (137.327 g/mol Ba + 2 × (35.453 g/mol Cl)) = 0.194 mol $BaCl_2$
       0.194 mol $BaCl_2$ × (2 mol NaCl / 1 mol $BaCl_2$) = 0.389 mol NaCl
       0.389 mol NaCl × (22.9898 g/mol Na + 35.453 g/mol Cl) = 22.7 g NaCl produced

61.   88.0 g C_3H_8 ÷ (3 × (12.0115 g/mol C) + 8 × (1.00794 g/mol H)) = 2.00 mol C_3H_8
       2.00 mol C_3H_8 × (3 mol CO_2 / 1 mol C_3H_8) = 6.00 mol CO_2
       6.00 mol CO_2 × (12.0115 g/mol C + 2 × (15.9994 g/mol O)) = 264 g CO_2

63. (a) The action of hydrochloric acid on zinc is a redox reaction (reduction-oxidation). The zinc is oxidized (it loses electrons to go from a neutral charge to a +2 charge) and the hydrogen is reduced (it gains electrons to go from a +1 charge to a neutral charge).
    (b) The burning of gun cotton is a combustion reaction. The statement that it leaves almost no ash after ignition implies that its combustion is nearly complete–the chemical composition is such that the reaction with oxygen produces only carbon dioxide gas, water vapor, and nitrogen gas.
    (c) The production of a solid from two solutions is a precipitate reaction. The reaction of chloride ion with silver nitrate solution to produce solid silver chloride is an excellent forensic science application of this chemical principle.
    (d) The key word in this question is "acid." That gives the hint that this is an acid-base reaction. In fact, it is a neutralization reaction where the milk of magnesia is the base and stomach acid (as it refluxes into the esophagus) is the acid.

65.   In the diagram, there are three maroon diatomic molecules and seven blue diatomic molecules. In the reaction represented, one maroon diatomic molecule reacts with three blue diatomic molecules to form two molecules.
       Based on the maroon diatomic molecules, (3 × (2 molecules / 1 reactant) = 6) six product molecules could possibly be formed.

Based on the blue diatomic molecules, (7 × (2 molecules / 3 reactants) = 4.67 ≈ 4) four product molecules could possibly be formed. (This is assuming that we are dealing with discrete molecules and not some quantity of molecules, such as moles.)
Therefore, the blue diatomic molecules are the limiting reactant and the theoretical yield is four product molecules.

67. To determine the limiting reactant, first determine the number of moles of each reactant:

75.0 g $Fe(NO_3)_3$ ÷ (55.845 g/mol Fe + 3 × (14.00674 g/mol N) + 9 × (15.9994 g/mol O)) = 0.31009698… mol $Fe(NO_3)_3$ ≈ 0.310 mol $Fe(NO_3)_3$
25.0 g KOH ÷ (39.0983 g/mol K + 15.9994 g/mol O + 1.00794 g/mol H) = 0.445588… mol KOH ≈ 0.446 mol KOH

Remember, though, that the reactant with the lowest number of moles is not necessarily the limiting reactant. You also have to determine how many moles of product are produced from each reactant. Since the question is asking about $Fe(OH)_3$, that is the product we will use.

0.310 mol $Fe(NO_3)_3$ × (1 mol $Fe(OH)_3$ / 1 mol $Fe(NO_3)_3$) = 0.310 mol $Fe(OH)_3$ produced from $Fe(NO_3)_3$
0.446 mol KOH × (1 mol $Fe(OH)_3$ / 3 mol KOH) = 0.148666… mol $Fe(OH)_3$ ≈ 0.149 mol $Fe(OH)_3$ produced from KOH

Since fewer moles of $Fe(OH)_3$ are produced from KOH, it is the limiting reactant (even though there is a larger number of moles of KOH than $Fe(NO_3)_3$!).

0.149 mol $Fe(OH)_3$ × (55.845 g/mol Fe + 3 × (15.9994 g/mol O) + 3 × (1.00794 g/mol H)) = 15.92318598 g $Fe(OH)_3$ ≈ 15.9 g $Fe(OH)_3$ theoretical yield for the reaction.

69. Iodine ($I_2(s)$) is a halogen (group 17) in period 5. Phosphorus ($P_4(s)$) is in group 15 and period 3. Lithium metal (Li(s)) is an alkali metal (group 1) in period 2.

71. 125.0 g $C_7H_5N_3O_6$ ÷ (7 × (12.0115 g/mol C) + 5 × (1.00794 g/mol H) + 3 × (14.0067 g/mol N) + 6 × (15.9994 g/mol O)) = 0.550329… mol $C_7H_5N_3O_6$ ≈ 0.5503 mol $C_7H_5N_3O_6$
0.5503 mol $C_7H_5N_3O_6$ × (3 mol N_2 / 2 mol $C_7H_5N_3O_6$) = 0.82545 mol N_2 ≈ 0.8255 mol N_2
0.8255 mol N_2 × (2 × (14.0067 g/mol N)) = 23.1250617 g N_2 ≈ 23.13 g N_2 produced from the detonation of 125.0 g TNT.

73. 117.4 g N_2 ÷ (2 × (14.0067 g/mol N)) = 4.19085… mol N_2 ≈ 4.191 mol N_2
4.191 mol N_2 × (1 mol $C_3H_6N_6O_6$ ÷ 3 mol N_2) = 1.397 mol $C_3H_6N_6O_6$
1.397 mol $C_3H_6N_6O_6$ × (3 × (12.0115 g/mol C) + 6 × (1.00794 g/mol H) + 6 × (14.0067 g/mol N) + 6 × (15.9994 g/mol O)) = 310.305831 g $C_3H_6N_6O_6$ ≈ 310.3 g $C_3H_6N_6O_6$

75.   The unknown has color intensity approximately half-way between the 100 mg/L sample and the 200 mg/L sample. From this, a good estimate of the concentration of cyanide is 150 mg/L.

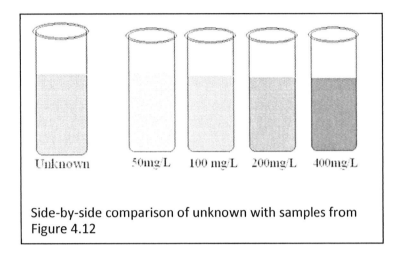

Side-by-side comparison of unknown with samples from Figure 4.12

77.   Some spectrophotometers simply yield an absorbance reading at one particular wavelength. If that is the case, the spectrophotometer should be set to a wavelength corresponding to the complementary color of yellow, which is violet. A good wavelength would be in the 450–500 nm range.

79.   The killer's fingerprints would have to be found on the inside of the Tylenol® bottle. The average customer does not open their over-the-counter medicine bottles in the store, especially not those that have the "tamper resistant" seals.

81. $Tl_2SO_4(aq) + BaCl_2(aq) \rightarrow 2\ TlCl\ (aq) + BaSO_4(s)$
      Next, determine the limiting reactant:

      4.06 g Tl_2SO_4 ÷ (2 × (204.3833 g/mol Tl) + 32.066 g/mol S + 4 × (15.9994 g/mol O))
      = 0.0080423... mol Tl_2SO_4 ≈ 0.00804 mol Tl_2SO_4
      0.00804 mol Tl_2SO_4 × (1 mol $BaSO_4$ / 1 mol Tl_2SO_4) = 0.00804 mol $BaSO_4$ produced from Tl_2SO_4
      4.41 g $BaCl_2$ ÷ (137.327 g/mol Ba + 2 × (35.453 g/mol Cl)) = 0.021178... mol $BaCl_2$
      ≈ 0.212 mol $BaCl_2$
      0.212 mol $BaCl_2$ × (1 mol $BaSO_4$ / 1 mol $BaCl_2$) = 0.212 mol $BaSO_4$ produced from $BaCl_2$

      Therefore, Thallium (I) Sulfate is the limiting reactant. Now we can determine the theoretical yield of $BaSO_4$:

      0.00804 mol $BaSO_4$ × (137.327 g/mol Ba + 32.066 g/mol S + 4 × (15.9994 g/mol O))
      = 1.87646... g $BaSO_4$ ≈ 1.88 g $BaSO_4$ theoretical yield.

83.   Scientifically speaking, it is important to use the phrase "was consistent with" rather than "was" because the scientist cannot travel backward in time to determine what took place in the past. Instead, it is only possible to do specific measurements that can indicate whether the evidence is consistent with or inconsistent with the proposed hypothesis within the context of the particular measurements being performed.

Chapter 5

Chemistry of Bonding: Structure and Function of Drug Molecules

1. Most single atoms do not have a full shell (sometimes called an octet) of valence (outermost) electrons. To obtain a full shell, they can either exchange (donate or accept) or share electrons. Two atoms can share a pair of electrons to form a bond:
    H· + H· → H· ·H → H–H
    This can also be represented as shown in Worked Example 1 on page 240.

3. Atoms form covalent bonds when they share electrons equally. Nonmetals tend to form covalent bonds when bonding with other nonmetals. Atoms form ionic bonds when they exchange (donate or accept) electrons. Metals tend to form ionic bonds with nonmetals.

5. When atoms exchange or share electrons, they achieve a full valence shell (sometimes called an octet). This is a stable configuration that minimizes the energy of the atoms present. This energy minimization is the reason why many chemical reactions proceed the way they do.

7. A double bond will form between two atoms when both atoms need the second bond to achieve a full valence shell. For example, oxygen is two electrons short of an octet. If each oxygen atom shares two electrons with the other, a double bond is formed.

9. Resonance structures show equivalent possible structures based on the placement of electrons in multiple bonds or lone pairs. They do not represent accurate bonding within the molecule because the actual bonding is some combination of the resonance structures. Crudely speaking, the actual structure is a sort of "average" of all possible resonance structures.

11. According to the VSEPR theory, electron regions around an atom will move until they are as far apart as possible. The number of electron regions determines the angle required between regions to allow maximum separation. The angle describes the electron geometry of the molecule.

13. The nature of the electron region does not affect the overall electron geometry of the molecule. However, the "size" of an electron region does depend on its nature (single bond, double bond, triple bond, lone pair). Lone pairs take up more space than bonds do, so they cause a distortion of the bond angles to make more space for themselves. This slightly alters the electron geometry.

15. As described in #13, the nature of electron regions slightly alters electron geometry. Since electron geometry determines the molecular geometry, the molecular geometry is also affected (albeit slightly) by the nature of the electron regions in the molecule.

17.   According to our textbook, stereoisomers occur when two compounds share the same chemical formula and the same connections between atoms, but exhibit differences in the way their atoms are arranged three-dimensionally. This is extremely significant in drug chemistry – different stereoisomers can have very different properties. The example given in the text is that l-methamphetamine is an ingredient in (legal) vapor-rub products while d-methamphetamine is an extremely addictive illegal drug.

19.   The molecular shape of neurotransmitters is the key function that controls their uptake into the uptake channel of the neuron. According to our textbook, the tunnel walls are strands of protein molecules arranged so that neurotransmitters of a particular shape and size may pass through.

21.   Cocaine and other illegal drugs cause a permanent change in brain function by causing destruction of uptake channels. The resulting damage to neurons is not repaired, often leading to depression and other symptoms.

23.   For Lewis dot structures, remember that the number of dots equals the number of valence electrons the atom possesses.

   (a) $\overset{\cdot}{\text{Sr}}\cdot$

   (b) $\cdot\overset{\cdot}{\text{Si}}\cdot$

   (c) $:\overset{\cdot\cdot}{\underset{\cdot}{\text{O}}}\cdot$

   (d) $:\overset{\cdot\cdot}{\underset{\cdot\cdot}{\text{Br}}}\cdot$

25.   For Lewis dot structures of ionic species, remember that the number of valence electrons must be adjusted based on the observed charge. Positive charges correspond to removal of electrons, and negative charges correspond to addition of electrons.

   (a) $\text{Na}^+ \ \text{Na}^+ \ \left[:\overset{\cdot\cdot}{\underset{\cdot\cdot}{\text{S}}}:\right]^{2-}$

   (b) $\text{Mg}^{2+} \left[:\overset{\cdot\cdot}{\underset{\cdot\cdot}{\text{Cl}}}:\right]^- \left[:\overset{\cdot\cdot}{\underset{\cdot\cdot}{\text{Cl}}}:\right]^-$

   (c) $\text{Sr}^{2+} \left[:\overset{\cdot\cdot}{\underset{\cdot\cdot}{\text{O}}}:\right]^{2-}$

   (d) $\text{Li}^+ \ \text{Li}^+ \ \text{Li}^+ \ \left[:\overset{\cdot\cdot}{\underset{\cdot\cdot}{\text{P}}}:\right]^{3-}$

27. $:\overset{\cdot\cdot}{\underset{\cdot\cdot}{\text{I}}}\!\!-\!\!\overset{\cdot\cdot}{\text{N}}\!\!-\!\!\overset{\cdot\cdot}{\underset{\cdot\cdot}{\text{I}}}:$

        $\overset{\cdot\cdot}{\underset{\cdot\cdot}{\text{I}}}:$

29.   (a)

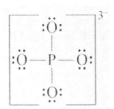

(b)

(c)

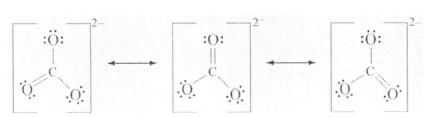

(d)

$$[\ddot{O} - H]^-$$

31.   (a)

:F —— P —— F:
|
: F :

(b) :O == N —— O·
↕
·O —— N == O:

(c) : Cl:
|
:Cl —— C —— Cl:
|
: Cl:

(d)   H —— As —— H
|
H

33. (a) CN^- has two electron domains: linear electron geometry
     (b) PO_4^{3-} has four electron domains: tetrahedral electron geometry
     (c) CO_3^{2-} has three electron domains: trigonal planar electron geometry
     (d) OH^- has four electron domains: tetrahedral electron geometry

35. (a) PF_3 has four electron domains: tetrahedral electron geometry
     (b) NO_2 has three electron domains: trigonal planar electron geometry
     (c) CCl_4 has four electron domains: tetrahedral electron geometry
     (d) AsH_3 has four electron domains: tetrahedral electron geometry

37. (a) CN^- has two electron domains, one of which is bonding: linear molecular geometry
     (b) PO_4^{3-} has four electron domains, all bonding: tetrahedral molecular geometry
     (c) CO_3^{2-} has three electron domains, all bonding: trigonal planar molecular geometry
     (d) OH^- has four electron domains, one bonding and three non-bonding: linear molecular geometry

39. (a) PF_3 has four electron domains, three of which are bonding: trigonal pyramidal molecular geometry
     (b) NO_2 has three electron domains, two of which are bonding: bent molecular geometry (120°)
     (c) CCl_4 has four electron domains, all bonding: tetrahedral molecular geometry
     (d) AsH_3 has four electron domains, three of which are bonding: trigonal pyramidal molecular geometry

41.

Electron Regions	Number of Lone Pairs	Electron Geometry	Molecular Geometry
2	0	linear	linear
3	1	trigonal planar	bent (120°)
4	0	tetrahedral	tetrahedral

43. (a) NO_2^-: trigonal planar electron geometry, bent molecular geometry

     (b) ClO_4^-: tetrahedral electron geometry, tetrahedral molecular geometry

     (c) ClO_2^-: tetrahedral electron geometry, bent molecular geometry

(d) NH_3: tetrahedral electron geometry, trigonal pyramidal molecular geometry

$$H - \overset{\cdot\cdot}{N} - H$$
$$|$$
$$H$$

45. (a) difference in electronegativity is $4.0 - 2.1 = 1.9$, therefore F–P bond is polar covalent ($\leftarrow$)
    (b) difference in electronegativity is $2.1 - 2.8 = -0.7$, therefore H–Br bond is polar covalent ($\rightarrow$)
    (c) difference in electronegativity is $3.0 - 3.0 = 0.0$, therefore N–Cl bond is non-polar covalent
    (d) difference in electronegativity is $2.5 - 2.5 = 0.0$, therefore S–C bond is non-polar covalent

47. (a) difference in electronegativity is $3.5 - 2.1 = 1.4$, therefore O–P bond is polar covalent ($\leftarrow$)
    (b) difference in electronegativity is $2.5 - 2.4 = 0.1$, therefore I–Se bond is nonpolar covalent
    (c) difference in electronegativity is $2.8 - 3.0 = -0.2$, therefore Br–N bond is nonpolar covalent
    (d) difference in electronegativity is $3.0 - 2.5 = 0.5$, therefore C–Se bond is nonpolar covalent

49. (a) P–F bonds are polar [$2.1 - 4.0 = -1.9$] and the molecule has a nonbonding electron pair; we would predict that the molecule is polar overall.
    (b) N–O bonds are polar [$3.0 - 2.5 = 0.5$] and the molecule has a nonbonding electron pair; polar molecule overall
    (c) C–Cl bonds are polar [$2.5 - 3.0 = -0.5$], but the molecule has no nonbonding electron pairs and all bond polarities cancel; nonpolar molecule overall
    (d) As–H bonds are nonpolar [$2.2 - 2.5 = -0.3$], but the molecule has a nonbonding electron pair; slightly polar molecule overall

51. Immunoassays are a screening method because they do not provide definite identification of a chemical compound. Because molecular geometry is an important part of how the immunoassay functions, it is possible for a molecule that has similar shape to an antigen (or its antibody) to cause the same reaction in the immunoassay as the target molecule. This could lead to a false positive if a confirmative test was not administered.

53. Oxygen at top of ring (tetrahedral, four electron regions); oxygen to right side of ring, double-bonded to carbon (trigonal planar, three electron regions)

55. The negative results from the GC-MS test could provide sufficient "reasonable doubt" that a conviction may not have been secured if the defense had properly challenged the evidence. There is significant possibility for cross-reactivity in RIA, so it is possible that the tissue samples did not really have LSD present.

57. Physical evidence should always be more important in a criminal trial than circumstantial evidence. Because the physical evidence in the Martin case was not convincing, it may be possible for the prosecution (and the defense) to use circumstantial evidence to try and bolster their case. However, circumstantial evidence is never stronger than physical (scientific) evidence.

59. If I was a jury member, my complaint would be that the medical examiner did not sufficiently establish the cause of death to warrant a conviction. Arguments and circumstantial evidence are meaningless without a scientific indication of the actual cause of death and an actual physical link between the suspect and the cause of death.

Chapter 6

Properties of Solutions I: Aqueous Solutions

1. A solvent is a substance into which a solute can dissolve. The most common solvent on Earth is water (which is why it is sometimes referred to as the "universal solvent").

3. Strong electrolytes conduct electricity in solution by the motion of the ions through the solvent. Cations (positively charged ions) move toward the cathode (negatively charged electrode where reduction takes place), and anions (negatively charged ions) move toward the anode (positively charged electrode where oxidation takes place).

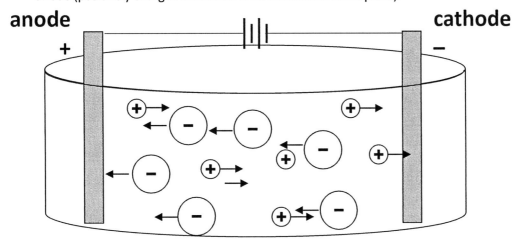

5. Electrolytes are substances that conduct electricity when dissolved in solution. Nonelectrolytes do not conduct electricity when they are dissolved. NaCl is an electrolyte, and sugar ($C_{12}H_{22}O_{11}$) is a nonelectrolyte.

7. Spectator ions do not participate in precipitation reactions. They simply balance the charges of the ions that do participate and are left behind in solution as the solid precipitate forms. It is possible for a precipitation reaction to occur without spectators, but only if all the ions in solution become part of the precipitate (quite an unusual situation).

9. The total ionic equation is a more accurate depiction of what's occurring in solution; it shows all ions and species that are present and the form in which they are present.

11. A saturated solution is one where the dissolved solute is in equilibrium with undissolved solute. A good example of this is when sugar is added to iced tea and much of the sugar remains at the bottom of the glass. The solution has become saturated with sugar. An unsaturated solution has all the solute completely dissolved. The unsaturated solution is uniform throughout and does not have any undissolved solute present.

13.   A supersaturated solution can be prepared by heating the solvent above room temperature. The solubility of most solid substances increases as the temperature increases, so more of the solid will dissolve. Once the solid has dissolved, allowing the solution to cool back to room temperature will cause a supersaturated solution to form. In practice, this can be very difficult to do – sometimes cooling the solution back to room temperature will cause the solute to precipitate from solution instead of remaining in the supersaturated solution.

15.   An acid is a substance that produces hydrogen ions (H^+) (sometimes called hydronium ions, H_3O^+) when dissolved in water. A base is a substance that produces hydroxide ions (OH^-) when dissolved in water. Acids dissolve to make solutions with low pH (less than 7), and bases dissolve to make solutions with high pH (greater than 7).

17.   Weak acids are not inherently safer than strong acids; safety is dependent on the concentration and type of acid. A highly concentrated weak acid can be more dangerous than a dilute strong acid.

19.   Bases can undergo neutralization reactions:
$$H^+(aq) + OH^-(aq) \rightarrow H_2O(l)$$
Bases can also undergo saponification reactions:
$$OH^-(aq) + grease\ (s) \rightarrow soap\ (aq)$$

21.   In everyday language, salt refers to table salt, which is sodium chloride (NaCl). When a chemist uses the term salt, he or she is referring to one of a number of ionic compounds. Sodium chloride is one particular example of these compounds. They are made up of positively charged cations and negatively charged anions combined to make a compound that has no overall charge.

23.   As your textbook states, the concept of pH was developed as a way of expressing the acidity of a solution. It is described as being the "power of hydrogen" and was developed in 1909 by Søren Sørenson.

25.   A buffer is a solution that resists changes in pH. It is a combination of a weak acid and the anion produced from neutralizing the weak acid; it works by having the weak acid (or the anion) reacting with the base (or the acid) as it is added to keep it from changing the pH of the solution significantly.

27.   Ionic compounds are electrolytes. Most molecular compounds are nonelectrolytes (although a few are weak electrolytes, but they are easily identified).
        (a) $Fe(NO_3)_3$ – electrolyte
        (b) C_2H_5OH – nonelectrolyte
        (c) HNO_3 – electrolyte
        (d) SO_2 – electrolyte (forms H_2SO_3 when dissolved in water)

29.   Ionic compounds are electrolytes. Most molecular compounds are nonelectrolytes (although a few are weak electrolytes, but they are easily identified).
        (a) HF – weak electrolyte
        (b) NaCl – strong electrolyte
        (c) H_2SO_4 – strong electrolyte
        (d) H_2CO_3 – weak electrolyte

31.   Use the solubility rules.
       (a) $FeCO_3$ is insoluble.   (b) $SrCO_3$ is insoluble.
       (c) $PbSO_4$ is insoluble.   (d) Li_2SO_4 is soluble.

33.   Balance the equation step by step until every element has been balanced. It may be useful to
       treat sulfate as a polyatomic ion rather than looking at sulfur and oxygen by themselves.
       $Na_2SO_4(aq) + CaCl_2(aq) \rightarrow NaCl(aq) + CaSO_4(s)$ SO_4, Ca balanced
       $Na_2SO_4(aq) + CaCl_2(aq) \rightarrow 2\ NaCl(aq) + CaSO_4(s)$ all balanced

       The total ionic equation is obtained by breaking all aqueous ionic compounds into their
       individual solvated ions. Remember that solid ionic compounds are not separated into the
       individual ions:

       $2\ Na^+(aq) + SO_4^{2-}(aq) + Ca^{2+}(aq) + 2\ Cl^-(aq) \rightarrow 2\ Na^+(aq) + 2\ Cl^-(aq) + CaSO_4(s)$

       The net ionic equation is obtained by eliminating any spectator ions from the equation. In this
       case, sodium and chloride ions are both spectators:

       $SO_4^{2-}(aq) + Ca^{2+}(aq) \rightarrow CaSO_4(s)$

       It is customary to write the cations first in the net ionic equation just as we do in the formula
       for the ionic compound that results:
       $Ca^{2+}(aq) + SO_4^{2-}(aq) \rightarrow CaSO_4(s)$

35.   The first step is to write correct formulas for each of the compounds.
       Aluminum nitrate + sodium sulfide $\rightarrow$ Aluminum(III) sulfide + sodium nitrate
       $Al(NO_3)_3 + Na_2S \rightarrow Al_2S_3 + NaNO_3$

       Next, determine the phases using the solubility rules.
       $Al(NO_3)_3(aq) + Na_2S(aq) \rightarrow Fe_2S_3(s) + NaNO_3(aq)$

       Now, balance the equation step by step. Grouping the acetate ion together will simplify things
       for us
       $2\ Al(NO_3)_3(aq) + Na_2S(aq) \rightarrow Fe_2S_3(s) + NaNO_3(aq)$ Al balanced
       $2\ Al(NO_3)_3(aq) + 3\ Na_2S(aq) \rightarrow Fe_2S_3(s) + NaNO_3(aq)$ Al, S balanced
       $2\ Al(NO_3)_3(aq) + 3\ Na_2S(aq) \rightarrow Fe_2S_3(s) + 6\ NaNO_3(aq)$ All balanced

       The total ionic equation is generated by separating the aqueous ionic compounds:

       $2\ Al^{3+}(aq) + 6\ NO_3^-(aq) + 6\ Na^+(aq) + 3\ S^{2-}(aq) \rightarrow Fe_2S_3(s) + 6\ Na^+(aq) + 6\ NO_3^-(aq)$

       The net ionic equation is generated by eliminating the sodium and acetate ion spectators:
            $2\ Al^{3+}(aq) + 3\ S^{2-}(aq) \rightarrow Al_2S_3(s)$

37.   There can be several approaches to this problem.   The most direct is to convert the concentration expressed in the problem (in g/mL) to units of g/100 mL. Then it is easy to see if the solution is saturated (the concentration is equal to 48.0 g/100 mL), unsaturated (less than that value), or supersaturated (greater than that value). (Alternatively, the solubility can be converted to g/mL and the concentration in g/mL can be compared to this value.)

   (a) 118 g NaCN in 250 mL is the same as 47.2 g/100 mL; this solution is unsaturated.

   (b) 12.0 g NaCN in 25.0 mL is the same as 48.0 g/100 mL; this solution is saturated.

   (c) 3.95 g NaCN in 8.33 mL is the same as 47.4 g/100 mL; this solution is unsaturated.

   (d) 214 mg NaCN in 0.400 mL is the same as 53.5 g/100 mL; this solution is supersaturated.

39.   Since a saturated solution is 50.0 g/100 mL, start there. Then multiply by the volume of solution desired (being sure to convert the volume units to mL so that they cancel!)

   (a) $(50.0 \text{ g} \div 100 \text{ mL}) \times 0.500 \text{ L} \times (1 \text{ mL} \div 10^{-3} \text{ L}) = 25.0 \text{ g KCN}$ to make a saturated solution

   (b) $(50.0 \text{ g} \div 100 \text{ mL}) \times 5.15 \text{ mL} = 2.58 \text{ g}$ of KCN to make a saturated solution

   (c) $(50.0 \text{ g} \div 100 \text{ mL}) \times 2.25 \text{ L} \times (1 \text{ mL} \div 10^{-3} \text{ L}) = 1{,}130 \text{ g}$ of KCN to make a saturated solution

   (d) $(50.0 \text{ g} \div 100 \text{ mL}) \times 250.0 \text{ mL} = 125 \text{ g}$ of KCN to make a saturated solution

41.   Molarity is a concentration unit of moles solute per liters of solution. We need to convert the masses to moles using the molar mass and then divide by the volume of solution in liters.

   (a) 31.45 g NaCl in 2.00 L

      31.45 g NaCl ÷ (22.98977 g/mol Na + 35.453 g/mol Cl) = 0.5381332... mol NaCl ≈ 0.5381 mol NaCl

      0.5381 mol NaCl ÷ 2.00 L = 0.2691 mol/L NaCl = 0.2691 M NaCl

   (b) 14.41 g MgS in 0.500 L

      14.41 g MgS ÷ (24.3050 g/mol Mg + 32.066 g/mol S) = 0.255627... mol MgS ≈ 0.256 mol MgS

      0.256 mol MgS ÷ 0.500 L = 0.0511 mol/L MgS = 0.0511 M MgS

   (c) 0.4567 g CuSO$_4$ in 630.0 mL

      0.4567 g CuSO$_4$ ÷ (63.546 g/mol Cu + 32.066 g/mol S + 4 × (15.9994 g/mol O)) = 0.00286135... mol CuSO$_4$ ≈ 0.002861 mol CuSO$_4$

      0.002861 mol CuSO$_4$ ÷ 0.6300 L = 0.004542 mol/L CuSO$_4$ = 0.004542 M CuSO$_4$

   (d) 25.5 mg NaCN in 10.0 mL

      0.0255 g NaCN   ÷ (22.98977 g/mol Na + 12.0115 g/mol C + 14.0067 g/mol N) = 5.20323... × 10^{-4} mol NaCN ≈ 5.20 × 10^{-4} mol NaCN

      5.20 × 10^{-4} mol NaCN ÷ 0.0100 L = 0.0520 mol/L NaCN = 0.0520 M NaCN

43.   To obtain moles, first convert the solution volumes into liters. Then, multiply the molarity (M = mol/L) by the volume in liters to obtain the number of moles.

   (a) 75.0 mL of 0.997 M CaCO$_3$:   0.0750 L × 0.997 M = 0.0748 mol CaCO$_3$

   (b) 25.0 mL of 2.50 M CaCO$_3$:   0.0250 L × 2.50 M = 0.0625 mol CaCO$_3$

   (c) 175 mL of 0.501 M CaCO$_3$:   0.175 L × 0.501 M = 0.0877 mol CaCO$_3$

   (d) 0.85 L of 3.42 M CaCO$_3$:   0.85 L × 3.42 M = 2.91 mol CaCO$_3$

45.   Since we already determined the number of moles of CaCO$_3$ in #43, we can multiply this by the molar mass of CaCO$_3$ to determine the number of grams.

      40.078 g/mol Ca + 12.0115 g/mol C + 3 × 15.9994 g/mol O = 100.0877 g/mol CaCO$_3$

   (a) 0.0748 mol CaCO$_3$ × 100.0877 g/mol CaCO$_3$ = 7.49 g CaCO$_3$

   (b) 0.0625 mol CaCO$_3$ × 100.0877 g/mol CaCO$_3$ = 6.26 g CaCO$_3$

   (c) 0.0877 mol CaCO$_3$ × 100.0877 g/mol CaCO$_3$ = 8.78 g CaCO$_3$

   (d) 2.91 mol CaCO$_3$ × 100.0877 g/mol CaCO$_3$ = 291 g CaCO$_3$

47.   We can use the dilution equation: $M_1V_1 = M_2V_2$. Solving for M_2, $M_2 = M_1V_1 \div V_2$. Since we are using the same initial solution in each case, we can also calculate the number of moles of HCl used and then divide by the new solution volume in liters. Using that approach,
$12.1\ M \times 0.1000\ L = 1.21\ mol\ HCl$
(a) $1.21\ mol\ HCl \div 0.1250\ L = 9.68\ mol/L = 9.68\ M\ HCl$
(b) $1.21\ mol\ HCl \div 2.00\ L = 0.605\ mol/L = 0.605\ M\ HCl$
(c) $1.21\ mol\ HCl \div 1.50\ L = 0.807\ mol/L = 0.807\ M\ HCl$
(d) $1.21\ mol\ HCl \div 0.6250\ L = 1.94\ mol/L = 1.94\ M\ HCl$

49.   Using the dilution equation: $M_1V_1 = M_2V_2$. Solving for V_1, $V_1 = M_2V_2 \div M_1$.
(a) $V_1 = 2.15\ M \times 5.00\ L \div 12.1\ M = 0.888\ L = 888\ mL$
(b) $V_1 = 3.50\ M \times 1.00\ L \div 12.1\ M = 0.289\ L = 289\ mL$
(c) $V_1 = 0.650\ M \times 2.00\ L \div 12.1\ M = 0.107\ L = 107\ mL$
(d) $V_1 = 0.250\ M \times 0.100\ L \div 12.1\ M = 0.00207\ L = 2.07\ mL$

51.   (a) H_2CO_3 = carbonic acid, weak acid
(b) HNO_3 = nitric acid, strong acid
(c) H_3PO_4 = phosphoric acid, weak acid
(d) H_2SO_4 = sulfuric acid, strong acid

53.   The reaction of sulfur trioxide and water:
$$SO_3(g) + H_2O(l) \rightarrow H_2SO_4(aq)$$

55.   (a) $2\ K(s) + 2\ H_2O(l) \rightarrow 2\ KOH(aq) + H_2(g)$
(b) $2\ Rb(s) + 2\ H_2O(l) \rightarrow 2\ RbOH(aq) + H_2(g)$
(c) $Sr(s) + 2\ H_2O(l) \rightarrow Sr(OH)_2(aq) + H_2(g)$
(d) $Mg(s) + 2\ H_2O(l) \rightarrow Mg(OH)_2(s) + H_2(g)$

57.   (a) $K_2O(s) + H_2O(l) \rightarrow 2\ KOH(aq)$
(b) $Rb_2O(s) + H_2O(l) \rightarrow 2\ RbOH(aq)$
(c) $SrO(s) + H_2O(l) \rightarrow Sr(OH)_2(aq)$
(d) $MgO(s) + H_2O(l) \rightarrow 2\ Mg(OH)_2(aq)$

59.   Neutralization of acetic acid ($HC_2H_3O_2$) with ammonium hydroxide (NH_4OH):
$$HC_2H_3O_2(aq) + NH_4OH(aq) \rightarrow H_2O(l) + NH_4C_2H_3O_2(aq)$$

61.   (a) vinegar: acid, acetic acid, $HC_2H_3O_2$, weak electrolyte
(b) 2000 flushes toilet cleaner: base, sodium hypochlorite, $NaClO$, strong electrolyte
(c) car battery: acid, sulfuric acid, H_2SO_4, strong electrolyte
(d) carbonated soft drink: acid, carbonic, and phosphoric acids, H_2CO_3 and H_3PO_4, weak electrolytes

63. $pH = -\log[H^+]$
(a) $-\log(0.0027\ M) = 2.6$
(b) $-\log(0.075\ M) = 1.1$
(c) $-\log(0.091\ M) = 1.1$
(d) $-\log(3.08 \times 10^{-5}) = 4.5$

65.   To convert the concentrations in g/mL units to molarity, we must convert the grams into moles by dividing by the molar mass and convert the 100 mL into L.

KCN: 50 g/100 mL   50 g ÷ (39.0983 g/mol K + 12.0115 g/mol C + 14.0067 g/mol N) = 0.767854... mol KCN
                          0.77 mol ÷ 0.100 L = 7.7 M

NaCN: 48 g/100 mL   48 g ÷ (22.98977 g/mol Na + 12.0115 g/mol C + 14.0067 g/mol N) = 0.979432... mol NaCN
                          0.98 mol ÷ 0.100 L = 9.8 M

$Cu(CN)_2$: 0 g/100 mL   (Since it's zero, this one is easy to calculate): 0 M

$Cd(CN)_2$: 1.7 g/100 mL   1.7 g ÷ (112.411 g/mol Cd + 2 × (12.0115 g/mol C) + 2 × (14.0067 g/mol N)) = 0.01033765... mol $Cd(CN)_2$
                          0.010 mol ÷ 0.100 L = 0.10 M

67.   151.964 g/mol Eu + 3 × 35.453 g/mol Cl + 12 × 1.0079 g/mol H + 6 × 15.999 g/mol O = 366.4118 g/mol $EuCl_3 \cdot 6H_2O$
        1.00 g $EuCl_3 \cdot 6H_2O$ ÷ (366.4118 g/mol $EuCl_3 \cdot 6H_2O$) = 0.002729... mol ≈ 0.00273 mol $EuCl_3 \cdot 6H_2O$
        0.00273 mol $EuCl_3 \cdot 6H_2O$ ÷ 0.8000 L = 0.0034125 M ≈ 0.00341 M

69.   6 × 12.011 g/mol C + 8 × 1.0079 g/mol H + 7 × 15.999 g/mol O = 192.1222 g/mol $C_6H_8O_7$
        0.5000 L × 0.10 M = 0.05000 mol $C_6H_8O_7$
        0.05000 mol $C_6H_8O_7$ × 192.1222 g/mol $C_6H_8O_7$ = 9.60611 g ≈ 9.6 g $C_6H_8O_7$

71.   If the person has a mass of 70.0 kg, then the LD_{50} corresponds to:
        15 mg per 1 kg × 70.0 kg = 1050 mg = 1.05 g As_2O_3
        1.05 g As_2O_3 ÷ (2 × (74.92160 g/mol As) + 3 × (15.9994 g/mol O)) = 0.005307281... mol As_2O_3 ≈ 0.00531 mol As_2O_3
        The concentration is 0.00531 mol ÷ 0.355 L = 0.01495774... mol/L ≈ 0.0150 M

73. $CaO(s) + H_2O(l) \rightarrow Ca(OH)_2(aq)$
        The poem says that the man was chained ("with fetters on each foot") "wrapped in a sheet of flame!" While quicklime does burn the skin, it doesn't do so with a sheet of flame. It slowly dissolves away the flesh off a man's body. Wilde exaggerates its use somewhat, but it still makes an interesting forensic science-related poem.

75.   The difference between the two statements is that the presence of coke doesn't necessarily mean that $TlNO_3$ is present. Saying that "the samples are consistent with thallium nitrate being added" is more specific.

77.   As we calculated in question #72, only 350 mg (0.350 g) of potassium cyanide are needed to reach the LD_{50} for humans with body mass 70 kg. This is an extremely small amount of material and could easily be added to an altered sample of Tylenol® capsules or tablets. The high solubility of potassium cyanide (50 g/100 mL of water) would also make it easy to poison Tylenol® capsules or tablets.

Chapter 7

Properties of Solutions II: Intermolecular Forces and Colligative Properties

1. Polar solvents have dipole–dipole forces. They also have London dispersion forces (van der Waals forces), but these are much weaker (and therefore less important) than the dipole–dipole forces.

3. Hydrogen bonds form between molecules that have hydrogen bonded to nitrogen, oxygen, or fluorine atoms within them.

5. London dispersion forces are the weakest type of intermolecular forces because the induced dipole is only formed temporarily. Since it only exists for a limited amount of time, the force is weaker.

7. When ionic compounds are dissolved in a polar solvent, they dissociate. This leads to the development of ion–dipole forces within the solution.

9. The dissolution of a nonpolar molecule in a polar solvent takes place because of the dipole–induced dipole force. London dispersion forces also provide a minor contribution to the attractive forces between a nonpolar molecule and a polar solvent. This combined attractive force allows oxygen gas to dissolve in water.

11. In reality, there are many more water molecules than either potassium ions (large dark gray spheres) or sulfide ions (smaller light gray spheres). However, that would make the drawing much too cluttered. The ratio of two potassium ions for every sulfide ion is required for the ionic compound to be uncharged overall.

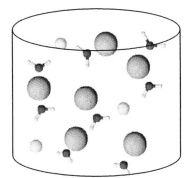

13. Gasoline is composed of a mixture of several different nonpolar compounds (e.g., octane, C_8H_{18}). Because grease is composed of various nonpolar compounds, gasoline is a good solvent to dissolve away the grease from mechanics' hands.

15. The rate of dissolving a soluble compound is affected by temperature, surface area of solid, and rate of stirring.

17. Water only boils at 100°C when it is completely pure and the atmospheric pressure is the same as that at sea level. Since many researchers do experiments in locations where the atmospheric pressure is significantly different from that at sea level, it is important to calibrate thermometers using other criteria.

19. The boiling point of a solution is the temperature at which the vapor pressure of the solution is equal to atmospheric pressure. We can observe this when bubbles form spontaneously within the solution and rise to the top of the solution.

21. The solute particles block solvent molecules from moving into the vapor phase by decreasing the number of solvent molecules available to escape into the vapor phase. This decreases the vapor pressure of the solution.

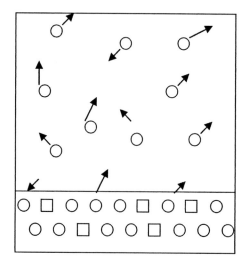

23. If saltwater has a freezing point of −4°C, then lowering the temperature to −5°C will require that the entire sample become a solid. All the liquid water molecules line up around the dissolved salt ions and form a crystal that eventually spreads through the entire sample to make a solid block of frozen saltwater. In the diagram below, circles represent water molecules, squares represent sodium ions, and triangles represent chloride ions. The precise arrangement of ions in the crystal can vary dramatically depending on concentration, but it is important to note that the number of sodium ions must equal the number of chloride ions in the sample.

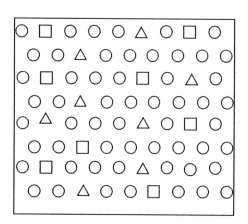

25.   Calcium chloride is not more efficient than sodium chloride at lowering the freezing point of water because there are three moles of ions formed for every 110.986 g of $CaCl_2$, while there are only two moles of ions formed for every 58.44277 g of NaCl. That means that more ions per gram are formed from sodium chloride than calcium chloride, making the sodium chloride more efficient.

27.   High salt concentrations used in pickling cause high osmotic pressures within the cells. Any bacteria or mold cells that attempt to survive in this environment will become extremely dehydrated and are unlikely to be successful.

29.   HPLC uses the solubility of various components in an eluting solvent. If the solvent and solute have similar intermolecular forces, the solute will be very soluble in the solvent and will elute quickly. If the solute has intermolecular forces similar to the stationary phase of the column, it will elute more slowly. By controlling the composition of the solvent, HPLC controls the rate at which solutes elute and give an indication of the composition of a mixture of liquids.

31.   If the volume of the regular octahedron is 1 cm^3 and the equation is $V = (\sqrt{2}/3)a^3$, then we can solve for a:
       $a = 3\sqrt{(3\,V/\sqrt{2})} = 1.284898293 \text{ cm}$
       Therefore, the surface area can be calculated:
       S.A. $= 2\sqrt{3}\,a^2 = 5.719105758 \text{ cm}^2 \approx 5.7 \text{ cm}^2$
       A sphere has a volume of $(4\pi/3)\,r^3$ and the surface area is $4\pi r^2$. If the volume of the sphere is 1 cm^3, the radius must be:
       $R = 3\sqrt{(3\,V/(4\pi))} = 0.2387324146 \text{ cm}$
       And the surface area is:
       S.A. $= 4\pi r^2 = 4.835975862 \text{ cm}^2 \approx 4.8 \text{ cm}^2$.
       The regular octahedron has 5.7/4.8 = 1.1875, or 19% more surface area than the sphere with equal volume.

33.   Polarizability is related to the number of electrons in an atom and the atomic size. In a given column of the periodic table, the higher the atomic number and the greater the polarizability: Be < Mg < Ca < Sr.

35.   (a) H_2O (polar): Since this molecule is polar, it has dipole–dipole forces. All molecules have London dispersion forces. In addition, this molecule also has hydrogen bonding because it has hydrogen atoms bonded to O.
       (b) CH_3OH (polar): Since this molecule is polar, it has dipole–dipole forces. All molecules have London dispersion forces. In addition, this molecule also has hydrogen bonding because it has a hydrogen atom bonded to O.
       (c) Br_2 (nonpolar): This molecule has only London dispersion forces.

37.   (a) Dipole–instantaneous dipole forces, London dispersion forces are present when O_2 is dissolved in water.
       (b) Hydrogen bonding, dipole–dipole forces, dipole–instantaneous dipole forces, and London dispersion forces are present when CH_3OH is dissolved in water.
       (c) Ion–dipole forces, hydrogen bonding, dipole–dipole forces, dipole–instantaneous dipole forces, and London dispersion forces are present when $NH_4C_2H_3O_2$ is dissolved in water.

39. HI will have a higher boiling point than HBr. Both compounds have dipole-dipole forces and London dispersion forces. Although HBr is slightly more polar than HI, HI has significantly stronger London dispersion forces.

41. 40.0 g / 100 mL at 20°C would be:
Unsaturated for KBr and Na_2SO_4
Supersaturated for KCl, NaCl, and KNO_3,

43. For KCl, the solubility from Figure 7.8 is
(a) 28 g / 100 mL at 10°C
(b) 35 g / 100 mL at 30°C
(c) 48 g / 100 mL at 60°C
(d) 60 g / 100 mL at 90°C

45. For KNO_3, the solutions would be saturated based on Figure 7.8
(a) 80.0 g at 53°C
(b) 20.0 g at 13°C
(c) 65.0 g at 46°C
(d) 30.0 g at 25°C

47. 0.30 M $CaCl_2$ has a total ion concentration of 0.90 M (one Ca^{2+} and two Cl^- ions)
0.25 M Na_3PO_4 has a total ion concentration of 1.00 M (three Na^+ and one PO_4^{3-} ions)
0.45 M LiI has a total ion concentration of 0.90 M (one Li^+ and one I^-)

Therefore, when put in order of decreasing vapor pressure:
C (0.45 M LiI) = A (0.30 M $CaCl_2$) > B (0.25 M Na_3PO_4)

49. The highest boiling point will result from the highest molality of ions or molecules in solution.
For the 0.66 m NaCl solution, 1.32 m total ions
For the 0.50 m Na_2S solution, 1.50 m total ions
For the 0.15 m $C_6H_{12}O_6$, 0.15 m total molecules

Therefore, the highest boiling point will be 0.50 m Na_2S followed by 0.66 m NaCl, and the lowest will be 0.15 m $C_6H_{12}O_6$.

51. $\Delta T_b = K_b m_{particles}$. $K_b = 0.512°C/m$ for water
For the 0.66 m NaCl solution, $\Delta T_b = 0.68°C$, so $T_b = 100.68°C$
For the 0.50 m Na_2S solution, $\Delta T_b = 0.77°C$, so $T_b = 100.77°C$
For the 0.15 m $C_6H_{12}O_6$, $\Delta T_b = 0.077°C$, so $T_b = 100.077°C$

53. In each case, we need the molality in order to look at the change in boiling point of the water. To accomplish this, we first need the number of moles of solute. Next, divide by the kilograms of solvent to get molality. After determining the total molality of all solute particles, use the boiling point elevation equation to determine the boiling point of the solution.

(a) KI: 39.098 g/mol K + 126.905 g/mol I = 166.003 g/mol

47.0 g KI ÷ 166.003 g/mol = 0.283 mol KI

0.283 mol KI ÷ 0. 5000 kg = 0.566 m KI

2 particles → 1.13 m solute → ΔT = 0.580°C; T = 100.58°C

(b) NH_4NO_3: 2 × (14.007 g/mol N) + 4 × (1.0079 g/mol H) + 3 × (15.999 g/mol O) = 80.0426 g/mol

28.0 g NH_4NO_3 ÷ 80.0426 = 0.350 mol NH_4NO_3

0.350 mol NH_4NO_3 ÷ 0.2500 kg = 1.40 m NH_4NO_3

2 particles → 2.80 m solute → ΔT = 0.716°C; T = 100.43°C

(c) $CO(NH_2)_2$: 12.011 g/mol C + 15.999 g/mol O + 2 × (14.007 g/mol N) + 4 × (1.0079 g/mol H) = 60.0556 g/mol

33.0 g $CO(NH_2)_2$ ÷ 60.0556 = 0.549 mol $CO(NH_2)_2$

0.549 mol $CO(NH_2)_2$ ÷ 0.1000 kg = 5.49 m $CO(NH_2)_2$

1 particle → 5.49 m solute → ΔT = 2.81°C; T = 102.81°C

55. T_f for pure water is 0.00°C.

(a) ΔT = −1.86 °C/m × 1.13 m solute = −2.10°C

T_f = −2.10°C

(b) ΔT = −1.86 °C/m × 2.80 m solute = −5.21°C

T_f = −5.21°C

(c) ΔT = −1.86 °C/m × 5.49 m solute = −10.2°C

T_f = −10.2°C

57. $\Delta T_f = K_f m_{particles}$. K_f = −1.86°C/m for water.

For the 0.66 m NaCl solution, ΔT = −2.5°C, so T_f = −2.5°C.

For the 0.50 m Na_2S solution, ΔT = −2.8°C, so T_f = −2.8°C.

For the 0.15 m $C_6H_{12}O_6$, ΔT = −0.28°C, so T_f = −0.28°C.

59. In each case, we need the molality in order to look at the change in boiling point of the water. To accomplish this, we first need the number of moles of solute. Next, divide by the kilograms of solvent to get molality. After determining the total molality of all solute particles, use the freezing point depression equation to determine the boiling point of the solution.

(a) $FeCl_3$: 55.845 g/mol K + 3 × (35.453 g/mol Cl) = 162.204 g/mol

13.2 g $FeCl_3$ ÷ 162.204 g/mol = 0.0814 mol $FeCl_3$

0.0814 mol $FeCl_3$ ÷ 0.0500 kg = 1.63 m $FeCl_3$

4 particles → 6.51 m solute → ΔT = −12.1°C, so T_f = −12.1°C

(b) $NaNO_3$: 22.990 g/mol Na + 14.007 g/mol N + 3 × (15.999 g/mol O) = 84.994 g/mol

149.0 g $NaNO_3$ ÷ 84.994 = 3.379 mol $NaNO_3$

3.379 mol $NaNO_3$ ÷ 0.3500 kg = 5.009 m $NaNO_3$

2 particles → 10.02 m solute → ΔT = −18.60°C, so T_f = −18.60°C

(c) $(NH_4)_2SO_4$: 2 × (14.007 g/mol N) + 8 × (1.0079 g/mol H) + 32.065 g/mol S + 4 (15.999 g/mol O) = 132.1392 g/mol

327.4 g $(NH_4)_2SO_4$ ÷ 132.1392 g/mol = 2.478 mol $(NH_4)_2SO_4$

2.478 mol $(NH_4)_2SO_4$ ÷ 2.20 kg = 1.126 m $(NH_4)_2SO_4$

3 particles → 3.379 m solute → ΔT = −6.29°C, so T_f = −6.29°C

61.   First, we determine ΔT. From that, we can use either K_f or K_b to determine the molality of glucose in the solution. Since glucose is a nonelectrolyte, there is only one glucose molecule for every solvent particle present.
       (a) $\Delta T_f = -2.8°C$; $m = -2.8°C\ /\ -1.86°C/m = 1.51$ m glucose
       (b) $\Delta T_b = +2.7°C$; $m = +2.7°C\ /\ 0.512°C/m = 5.27$ m glucose
       (c) $\Delta T_b = +1.3°C$; $m = +1.3°C\ /\ 0.512°C/m = 2.54$ m glucose

63.   The molar mass of glucose is $(6 \times (12.0115$ g/mol C$) + 12 \times (1.00794$ g/mol H$) + 6 \times (15.9994$ g/mol O$)) = 180.16068$ g/mol. Since there is 1.00 kg of solvent, the number of moles of solute present is equal to the molality of the solution. To determine the mass, multiply the number of moles by the molar mass.
       (a) 1.51 moles $C_6H_{12}O_6 = 272$ g $C_6H_{12}O_6$
       (b) 5.27 moles $C_6H_{12}O_6 = 949$ g $C_6H_{12}O_6$
       (c) 2.54 moles $C_6H_{12}O_6 = 458$ g $C_6H_{12}O_6$

65.   Osmosis naturally takes place to make solute concentrations the same on both sides of a membrane. Water molecules must pass through the membrane from the pure water to the seawater and solute particles must pass through the membrane from the seawater to the pure water.

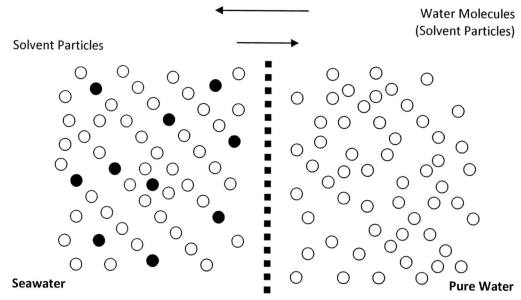

67.   Osmotic pressure, $\Pi = M R T$
      (a) NaF: 22.990 g/mol Na + 18.998 g/mol F = 41.988 g/mol
          16.3 g NaF ÷ 41.988 g/mol = 0.388 mol NaF
          0.388 mol NaF ÷ 1.00 L = 0.388 M NaF → 2 particles → 0.776 M solute
          20°C + 273.15 = 293 K
          $\Pi = M R T$ = 0.776 M × 0.0821 ((L atm)/(mol K)) × 293 K = 18.7 atm
      (b) $C_6H_{12}O_6$: 6 × (12.0115 g/mol C) + 12 × (1.00794 g/mol H) + 6 × (15.9994 g/mol O)) =
          180.16068 g/mol
          5.61 g $C_6H_{12}O_6$ ÷ 180.16068 g/mol = 0.0311 mol $C_6H_{12}O_6$
          0.0311 mol $C_6H_{12}O_6$ ÷ 1.00 L = 0.0311 M $C_6H_{12}O_6$ → 1 particle → 0.0311 M solute
          20°C + 273.15 = 293 K
          $\Pi = M R T$ = 0.0311 M × 0.0821 ((L atm)/(mol K)) × 293 K = 0.749 atm
      (c) $MgCl_2$: 24.305 g/mol Mg + 2 × (35.453 g/mol Cl) = 95.211 g/mol
          2.90 g $MgCl_2$ ÷ 95.211 g/mol = 0.0305 mol $MgCl_2$
          0.0305 mol $MgCl_2$ ÷ 0.5000 L = 0.0610 M $MgCl_2$ → 3 particles → 0.1830 M solute
          25°C + 273.15 = 298 K
          $\Pi = M R T$ = 0.1830 M × 0.0821 ((L atm)/(mol K)) × 298 K = 4.477 atm

69.   Alcohol permeates into the vitreous humor as soon as it is present in the bloodstream. If the deceased person consumed an extremely large portion of alcohol, the only way it would be in their bloodstream is if there was enough time for it to be absorbed through the stomach and small intestine. The answer to this question depends on the amount of time that passed between the drinking of the alcohol and the fatal accident. Other physical properties that could be examined to give more information would be freezing point and solubility in water.

71.   Having both boiling point and density information about the liquid sample will give a better indication of what is present. It is important to remember that the boiling point can change with the amount of dissolved solvent (boiling point elevation) and the density can also change depending on the amount of solvent. If the boiling point is measured and it matches the boiling point of propanol, the only way to be sure the liquid sample is propanol is if the density of the liquid is also a match. (In reality, other techniques such as infrared spectroscopy would be used to help identify the liquid. The more points of comparison between a sample and the known substance, the better!)

73.   Immunoassay methods rely on intermolecular forces to select for specific antibody/antigen pairs in the assay. The "lock-and-key" interactions between antigens and their associated antibodies are very specific applications of specific intermolecular forces. There are often different regions of the molecules, some of which are polar and some of which are nonpolar, in specific arrangements to give the specific interactions that allow for selective determination of a particular molecule.

75.   Trace levels of the compounds will be found in the young man's lungs, even if they were the cause of death, because the petroleum-based cleaners will gradually diffuse out of his lungs as the body was left for 16 hours from the time of death. The hypothesis might still be valid. The medical examiner will also look for petroleum-based compounds in the blood and other vital organs as an indication that the compounds were responsible for the young man's asphyxiation.

Chapter 8

Drug Chemistry

1. Historically (until the early nineteenth century, according to our textbook), organic compounds were those isolated from living or once-living organisms. They typically contained a high percentage of carbon, with some hydrogen, oxygen, and nitrogen (sometimes sulfur and phosphorus as well). Inorganic compounds were considered to be composed of the remaining elements (chiefly non-carbon based) of the periodic table. Rocks and minerals are classic examples of inorganic materials.

3. All alkanes have the formula C_nH_{2n+2}, where n is any positive integer. Alkanes have found utility as solvents and fuel sources.

5. Alkenes that contain only one double bond have the formula C_nH_{2n}, where n is any positive integer. Alkenes that contain only one triple bond have the formula C_nH_{2n-2}, where n is any positive integer.

7. Line structures are a shorthand notation of the structures of organic molecules. Each line represents a bond, and each corner (that has not been labeled otherwise) represents a carbon atom. Hydrogen atoms are implied; since carbon typically forms four bonds in organic compounds, hydrogen atoms are bonded to each carbon atom to bring its total number of bonds to four.

9. Two isomers have at least one physical property that is different. By rearranging the atoms in a molecule, we change the shape of the molecule. This impacts polarity, which in turn affects solubility, melting/freezing point, boiling/melting point, vapor pressure, and many other properties.

11. Resonance structures occur when more than one equivalent structure (where no atoms are rearranged) can be drawn for a molecule. It means that there is more than one way to arrange the electrons in the molecule and still have the same structure, and typically means that the molecule is more stable than it would be otherwise.

13. Although the Lewis structure of benzene contains C–C (carbon-carbon single bonds) and C=C (carbon-carbon double bonds) as well as C–H single bonds, all the carbon-carbon bond lengths in benzene are actually equal. This is because of resonance – the carbon-carbon bonds are actually intermediate in length between a single and a double bond. They can be thought of as an average between a single and a double bond, or a one-and-a-half bond, because of resonance.

15.   Ketones, ethers, and esters all contain oxygen atoms. Ketones have a C=O group (carbon double-bonded to oxygen) near the middle of the molecule (aldehydes have C=O at the end of the molecule, with a H atom bonded to the carbon). Ethers have an O atom within the molecule: C-O-C. Esters have a C=O group in the middle of the molecule that is bonded to an O atom, which is in turn bonded to another carbon atom (carboxylic acids have the C=O bonded to an OH group instead).

17.   The amine functional group is a nitrogen bonded to the molecule ($-NH_2$ or similar). A primary amine has only one carbon bonded to the nitrogen (CNH_2), while secondary and tertiary amines have two (C_2NH) and three (C_3N) carbons bonded to the nitrogen, respectively.

19.   Congeners are compounds that have the same functional groups as one another. Methanol (CH_3OH), ethanol (CH_3CH_2OH), 1-propanol ($CH_3CH_2CH_2OH$), 2-propanol ($CH_3CH(OH)CH_3$), and other alcohols are congeners.

21.   A Brønsted-Lowry base is a proton acceptor. An Arrhenius base is a compound that produces OH^- in aqueous solution (when dissolved in water). NaOH is a good example of an Arrhenius base. NH_3 is a Brønsted-Lowry base.

23.   (a) C_3H_8 is an alkane with three carbons, so it is called propane.
       (b) C_4H_{10} is an alkane with four carbons, so it is called butane.
       (c) CH_4 is an alkane with one carbon, so it is called methane.
       (d) C_7H_{16} is an alkane with seven carbons, so it is called heptane.

25.   (a) hexane – alkane with 6 carbon atoms, C_6H_{14}
       (b) butane – alkane with 4 carbon atoms, C_4H_{10}
       (c) pentane – alkane with 5 carbon atoms, C_5H_{12}
       (d) decane – alkane with 10 carbon atom, $C_{10}H_{22}$

27.   Remember, every carbon atom needs exactly four bonds, and each hydrogen atom can have only one.
       (a) CH_3
       (b) $CH_3CH_2CH_2CH_3$
       (c) CH_4
       (d) $CH_3CH_2CH_2CH_2CH_2CH_2CH_3$

29.   Each line represents a C-C bond, and each corner is a carbon atom.
       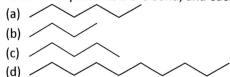

31. (a) propyne: C_3H_4, CH_3CCH,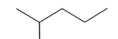

     (b) 3-nonene: C_9H_{18}, $CH_3CH_2CHCHCH_2CH_2CH_2CH_2CH_3$,

     (c) 2-heptene: C_7H_{14}, $CH_3CHCHCH_2CH_2CH_2CH_3$,

     (d) 1-pentyne: C_5H_8, $HCCCH_2CH_2CH_3$,

33. (a) butyne: two unique isomers: 1-butyne and 2-butyne
     (b) octyne: four unique isomers: 1-octyne, 2-octyne, 3-octyne, and 4-octyne
     (c) pentene: three unique isomers: 1-pentene, 2-pentene, and 3-pentene
     (d) propyne: one unique isomer

35. (a) 2-methylhexane
     (b) 3-methylheptane
     (c) 3-methylheptane
     (d) 2-methylpentane

37. (a) 2-methylheptane:

     (b) 4-ethyldecane:

     (c) 2-methylpentane:

     (d) 3-ethyloctane:

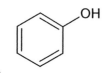

39.   (a) benzene: C_6H_6,

(b) phenol: benzene ring with alcohol group, C_6H_5OH,

(c) cyclobutane: four-membered ring alkane, C_4H_8,

(d) cyclohexane: six-membered ring alkane, C_6H_{12},

41.   (a) methoxypropane: ether with one-carbon and three-carbon chains, $CH_3OCH_2CH_2CH_3$
(b) ethoxyethane: ether with two two-carbon chains, $CH_3CH_2OCH_2CH_3$
(c) butoxyhexane: ether with four-carbon and six-carbon chains,
$CH_3CH_2CH_2CH_2OCH_2CH_2CH_2CH_2CH_2CH_3$
(d) propoxybutane: ether with three-carbon and four-carbon chains,
$CH_3CH_2CH_2OCH_2CH_2CH_2CH_3$

43.   (a) 2-hexanone: six-carbon chain with ketone on second carbon, $CH_3(C=O)CH_2CH_2CH_2CH_3$
(b) 2-pentanone: five-carbon chain with ketone on second carbon, $CH_3(C=O)CH_2CH_2CH_3$
(c) 3-heptanone: seven-carbon chain with ketone on third carbon, $CH_3CH_2(C=O)CH_2CH_2CH_2CH_3$
(d) 4-decanone: ten-carbon chain with ketone on fourth carbon,
$CH_3CH_2CH_2(C=O)CH_2CH_2CH_2CH_2CH_2CH_3$

45.   (a) methyl propanoate: ester with one-carbon alkyl and three-carbon acid group,
$CH_3O(C=O)CH_2CH_3$
(b) ethyl ethanoate: ester with two-carbon alkyl and two-carbon acid group,
$CH_3CH_2O(C=O)CH_3$
(c) ethyl propanoate: ester with two-carbon alkyl and three-carbon acid group,
$CH_3CH_2O(C=O)CH_2CH_3$
(d) propyl ethanoate: ester with three-carbon alkyl and two-carbon acid group,
$CH_3CH_2CH_2O(C=O)CH_3$

47.   (a) seven-carbon chain with ketone on third carbon, 3-hexanone
(b) ether with two-carbon and four-carbon chains, ethoxybutane
(c) ester with two-carbon alkyl and five-carbon acid group, ethyl pentanoate
(d) five-carbon chain with ketone on second carbon, 2-pentanone

49.   (a) pentylamine: $CH_3CH_2CH_2CH_2CH_2NH_2$
(b) ethylpropylamine: $CH_3CH_2NH(CH_2CH_2CH_3)$
(c) trimethylamine: $(CH_3)_3N$
(d) butylmethylpropylamine: $CH_3CH_2CH_2CH_2N(CH_3)CH_2CH_2CH_3$

51.   (a) pentylamine:

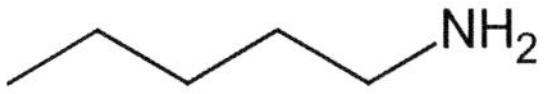

(b) ethylpropylamine:

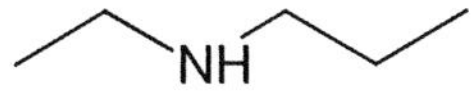

(c) trimethylamine:

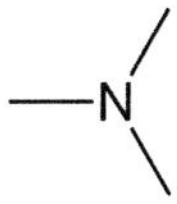

(d) butylmethylpropylamine:

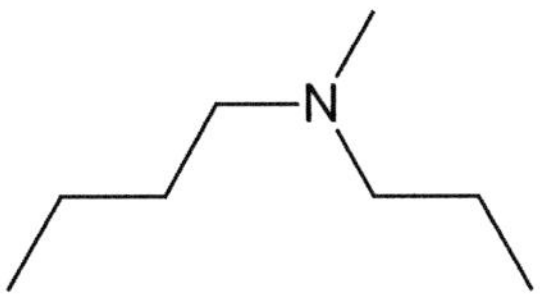

53.   (a) 2-butanol: four-carbon chain with alcohol on second carbon, $CH_3CH(OH)CH_2CH_3$
      (b) 2-propanol: three-carbon chain with alcohol on second carbon, $CH_3CH(OH)CH_3$
      (c) 1-pentanol: five-carbon chain with alcohol on first carbon, $CH_3CH_2CH_2CH_2CH_2OH$
      (d) 3-hexanol: six-carbon chain with alcohol on third carbon, $CH_3CH(OH)CH_2CH_2CH_2CH_3$

55.   (a) butanal: four-carbon straight-chain aldehyde, $CH_3CH_2CH_2(C=O)H$
      (b) hexanal: six-carbon straight-chain aldehyde, $CH_3CH_2CH_2CH_2CH_2(C=O)H$
      (c) ethanal: two-carbon straight-chain aldehyde, $CH_3(C=O)H$
      (d) octanal: eight-carbon straight-chain aldehyde, $CH_3CH_2CH_2CH_2CH_2CH_2CH_2(C=O)H$

57.   (a) ethanoic acid: two-carbon straight-chain carboxylic acid, $CH_3(C=O)OH$
      (b) octanoic acid: eight-carbon straight-chain carboxylic acid,
           $CH_3CH_2CH_2CH_2CH_2CH_2CH_2(C=O)OH$
      (c) decanoic acid: ten-carbon straight-chain carboxylic acid,
           $CH_3CH_2CH_2CH_2CH_2CH_2CH_2CH_2CH_2(C=O)OH$
      (d) butanoic acid: four-carbon straight-chain carboxylic acid, $CH_3CH_2CH_2(C=O)OH$

59.   (a) pentanal
      (b) hexanoic acid
      (c) 2-pentanol
      (d) hexanal

61. $CH_3CH_2CH_2CH_2CH_2CH_2OH$, 1-hexanol; $CH_3CH_2CH_2CH_2CH(OH)CH_3$, 2-hexanol;
      $CH_3CH_2CH(OH)CH_2CH_2CH_3$, 3-hexanol

63.   (a) 3-methylpropane is really butane. There are four carbon atoms in a linear chain.
      (b) 2-propylethane is really pentane. There are five carbon atoms in a linear chain.
      (c) 5-ethylheptane is really 3-ethylheptane. In naming compounds, always number the
           longest chain of carbon atoms to minimize the number given to each functional group.
      (d) 2-methylethane is really propane. There are three carbon atoms in a linear chain.

65.   (a) 3-propanoic acid is an incorrect name because the carboxylic acid group should receive
           the lowest possible position number. The correct name would be 1-propanoic acid, or
           simply propanoic acid.
      (b) 2-propanal does not exist because an aldehyde group cannot exist on the second carbon
           in a propane molecule. If there is a C=O group on the second carbon, it would be called 2-
           propanone, or simply propanone (commonly called acetone).

(c) 1-butanone does not exist because a ketone group cannot exist on a terminal carbon in a chain. If the C=O group is on the terminal carbon of a butane molecule, it would be called butanal.

(d) 3-butanol is more correctly named 2-butanol. The alcohol group should get the lowest possible position number, and the third carbon becomes the second carbon when the butane chain is numbered from the opposite group.

67. (a) 2-butanone is a neutral compound (ketone)
     (b) butanoic acid is an acid (carboxylic acid)
     (c) 1-propanol is an acid (alcohol)
     (d) methylamine is a base (amine)

69. Alcohols contain C–OH groups. Marijuana, GHB, 1,4-butanediol, lorazepam, psilocybin, morphine, and codeine all contain alcohol groups. Marijuana contains a phenol group.

71. Ketones contain C=O groups. Ketamine, OxyContin, and Vicodin contain ketone groups.

73. Ethers contain C–O–C groups. Heroin, marijuana, MDMA, MDA, OxyContin, Vicodin, codeine, and morphine all contain ether groups.

75. A benzene ring can be recognized by the six carbons in a ring with alternating double bonds. Methamphetamine, cocaine, heroin, marijuana, MDMA, MDA, ketamine, LSD, psilocybin, OxyContin, Vicodin, Ritalin, Xanax, lorazepam, clonazepam, codeine, and morphine all contain benzene rings.

77. Alcohol (ROH) $\rightarrow$ Aldehyde (RCOH) $\rightarrow$ Carboxylic acid (R(CO)OH)
     CH_3OH methanol $\rightarrow$ CH_2O methanal $\rightarrow$ CHO(OH) methanoic acid (formic acid)
     CH_3CH_2OH ethanol $\rightarrow$ CH_3CHO ethanal $\rightarrow$ $CH_3CO(OH)$ ethanoic acid (acetic acid)

79. Cadaverine: 1,5-pentanediamine: $NH_2CH_2CH_2CH_2CH_2CH_2NH_2$
     Putrescine: 1,4-butanediamine: $NH_2CH_2CH_2CH_2CH_2NH_2$

81. The functional group region of the FTIR evidence shows only the type of functional groups (structures like alcohols, aldehydes, ketones, amines, etc.) but gives little data in terms of how many of these structures are present in the molecule. Therefore, it would be very difficult to differentiate 1-butanol (one C-OH group) from 1,4-butanediol (two C-OH groups) by only examining this region. However, the fingerprint region of the FTIR evidence should be unique, and a visible difference is present between the two compounds in question.

83. Digoxin contains alcohol groups, ether groups, methyl groups, an alkene group, and an ester.

Chapter 9

Chemistry of Fire and Heat

1. Since the melting point of copper metal is nearly 1083°C, at both 50°C and 500°C, copper is a solid (temperature is BELOW the melting point). Solids are composed of atoms that are closely packed together. However, the atoms of copper are NOT stationary. There is enough thermal energy to cause them to "wiggle" about in their packed arrangements. As the temperature is raised from 50°C to 500°C, the atoms have more energy available and "wiggle" more than they did at the lower temperature. Once the two samples are brought together, energy is transferred as the atoms "bump" into each other, until the energy is distributed evenly throughout the sample, thus reaching thermal equilibrium (see figure below). The temperature at this point (≈275°C) is the average of the two initial temperatures since both samples were equal in mass [(500°C)(1/2 total mass) + (50°C)(1/2 total mass) = 250°C].

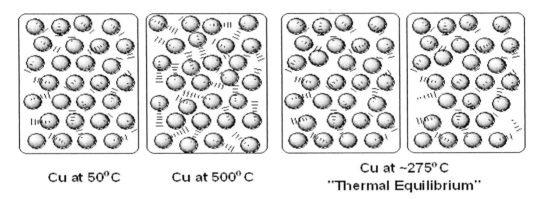

Cu at 50°C   Cu at 500°C   Cu at ~275°C "Thermal Equilibrium"

If the 500°C sample were twice the mass of the 50°C sample, then thermal equilibrium would be reached at 350°C because the 500°C mass represents 2/3 of the total mass [(500°C)(2/3 total mass) + (50°C)(1/3 total mass) = 350°C].

3. Heat is a form of energy that is transferred from hot objects to cold objects when they come in contact with one another. Temperature is a measurement of the average kinetic energy of the particles in a system, not a measurement of how much heat is in a system.

5. When a thermometer is placed in a solution, heat will flow either from the solution into the thermometer or from the thermometer into the solution. When this happens, the temperature of the solution will change. Thermometers are designed to minimize the amount of heat that flows in this case, but there is still a slight change in temperature whenever a thermometer is placed into a solution.

7. A backdraft forms when an excess of fuel is heated in the absence of oxygen. It can be prevented by ventilating the room (providing a source of oxygen from the air surrounding the room).

9. Organic compounds and certain metals and nonmetals can undergo combustion reactions.
    $CH_4(g) + 2 O_2(g) \rightarrow CO_2(g) + 2 H_2O(g)$
    $2 Ca(s) + O_2(g) \rightarrow 2 CaO(s)$
    $S_8(s) + 12 O_2(g) \rightarrow 8 SO_3(g)$
    (There are of course many other examples, but the above reactions demonstrate each of the three categories of substances.)

11. We can determine if an element within a compound is oxidized or reduced in a reaction by comparing the oxidation number of the element on each side of the chemical equation. The precaution to be followed is that oxidation is a loss of electrons and reduction is a gain of electrons. However, electrons have a negative charge, so oxidation results in an oxidation number that is more positive, and reduction results in an oxidation number that is less positive (more negative).

13. An endothermic reaction absorbs energy from its surroundings and an exothermic reaction releases energy into its surroundings. If the products have more energy than the reactants, the system must absorb energy from the surroundings (endothermic). If the products have less energy than the reactants, the system must release energy into the surroundings (exothermic).

15. Flashover takes place when heat from a fire in a small area rises to the ceiling and then spreads out across the room. As the fire progresses, the heated layer of smoke and gases just below the ceiling increases its temperature and thickness. Because the heat is restricted by the ceiling, it radiates downward, heating the remaining combustible materials in the room. This continues until the materials reach the auto-ignition temperature, where the materials have absorbed enough heat energy from the surroundings to overcome the activation energy of the combustion reaction. Flashover conditions can be prevented by ventilating the room at the ceiling, allowing the heated layer of smoke to escape.

17. Compounds with strong intermolecular forces have larger heat capacities than those with weak intermolecular forces. Compounds with hydrogen bonding (like water) have large heat capacities, and nonpolar compounds (like hexane) have small heat capacities.

19. Tile floor feels colder than carpeting even if they are at the same temperature because of the flow of heat from your bare foot into the material. Tile floor conducts heat more quickly than carpeting, so the heat flows more quickly from your foot into the tile than it does into the carpet. In addition, tile floor has a greater relative heat capacity than carpeting and can absorb more energy as heat before it reaches the same temperature as your foot. The net effect is that the tile floor feels cold and the carpet feels warmer.

21. Accelerants are often not completely consumed in a fire because the vaporization of the liquid fuel is an endothermic process. This lowers the temperature of the region surrounding the fuel to the point that there is insufficient heat for complete combustion to take place. As a result, there is usually some trace amount of accelerant remaining in the residue left after a fire.

23.   Crude oil is refined using a process called partial distillation. By heating the crude oil, compounds boil out of the mixture in quantities grouped by boiling point. According to our textbook, gasoline has components with boiling points from approximately 40°C to 220°C, and kerosene has components with boiling points ranging from 175°C to 270°C. Gasoline has more low molecular weight compounds and kerosene has more high molecular weight compounds.

25.   (a) 65.0 calories × (4.184 J / 1 cal) = 272 J = 2.72×10^2 J
       (b) 166.0 Calories × (1 kcal / 1 Cal) × (10^3 cal / 1 kcal) × (4.184 J / 1 cal) = 694,500 J
            = 6.945×10^5 J
       (c) 74.6 kilojoules × (10^3 J / 1 kJ) = 74,600 J = 7.46×10^4 J
       (d) 82.3 kilocalories × (10^3 cal / 1 kcal) × (4.184 J / 1 cal) = 344,000 J = 3.44×10^5 J

27.   (a) 11.0 Cal/g × (1 kcal / 1 Cal) × (10^3 cal / 1 kcal) × (4.184 J / 1 cal) = 46,024 J/g ≈ 46,000 J/g
       (b) 11.5 Cal/g × (1 kcal / 1 Cal) × (10^3 cal / 1 kcal) × (4.184 J / 1 cal) = 48,116 J/g ≈ 48,100 J/g
       (c) 10.0 Cal/g × (1 kcal / 1 Cal) × (10^3 cal / 1 kcal) × (4.184 J / 1 cal) = 41,840 J/g ≈ 41,800 J/g
       (d) 9.92 Cal/g × (1 kcal / 1 Cal) × (10^3 cal / 1 kcal) × (4.184 J / 1 cal) = 41,505.28 J/g ≈ 41,500 J/g

29.   (a) 43.3 MJ/kg × (10^6 J / 1 MJ) × (1 kg / 10^3 g) = 43,300 J/g = 4.33×10^4 J/g
       (b) 43.5 MJ/kg × (10^6 J / 1 MJ) × (1 kg / 10^3 g) = 43,500 J/g = 4.35×10^4 J/g
       (c) 43.7 MJ/kg × (10^6 J / 1 MJ) × (1 kg / 10^3 g) = 43,700 J/g = 4.37×10^4 J/g
       (d) 44.0 MJ/kg × (10^6 J / 1 MJ) × (1 kg / 10^3 g) = 44,000 J/g = 4.40×10^4 J/g

31.   In each case, add oxygen and put in the products carbon dioxide and water. Then, balance carbon. Then hydrogen, and finally oxygen. Last, adjust the coefficients to eliminate any fractions.

       (a) $CH_4 + O_2 \rightarrow CO_2 + H_2O$ (C is already balanced)
            $CH_4 + O_2 \rightarrow CO_2 + 2\,H_2O$ (C and H now balanced)
            $CH_4 + 2\,O_2 \rightarrow CO_2 + 2\,H_2O$ (Everything balanced, all whole numbers)
       (b) $C_5H_{12} + O_2 \rightarrow CO_2 + H_2O$ (Nothing balanced)
            $C_5H_{12} + O_2 \rightarrow 5\,CO_2 + H_2O$ (C is balanced)
            $C_5H_{12} + O_2 \rightarrow 5\,CO_2 + 6\,H_2O$ (C and H now balanced)
            $C_5H_{12} + 8\,O_2 \rightarrow 5\,CO_2 + 6\,H_2O$ (Everything balanced, all whole numbers)
       (c) $C_6H_{14}O + O_2 \rightarrow CO_2 + H_2O$ (Nothing balanced)
            $C_6H_{14}O + O_2 \rightarrow 6\,CO_2 + H_2O$ (C is balanced)
            $C_6H_{14}O + O_2 \rightarrow 6\,CO_2 + 7\,H_2O$ (C and H now balanced)
            $C_6H_{14}O + 9\,O_2 \rightarrow 6\,CO_2 + 7\,H_2O$ (All whole numbers)
       (d) $C_8H_{16}O + O_2 \rightarrow CO_2 + H_2O$ (Nothing balanced)
            $C_8H_{16}O + O_2 \rightarrow 8\,CO_2 + H_2O$ (C is balanced)
            $C_8H_{16}O + O_2 \rightarrow 8\,CO_2 + 8\,H_2O$ (C and H now balanced)
            $C_8H_{16}O + 11.5\,O_2 \rightarrow 8\,CO_2 + 8\,H_2O$ (O_2 has decimal coefficient)
            $2\,C_8H_{16}O + 23\,O_2 \rightarrow 16\,CO_2 + 16\,H_2O$ (Everything balanced)

33.   (a) Butane is a four-carbon chain: $CH_3CH_2CH_2CH_3$, C_4H_{10}

$C_4H_{10} + O_2 \rightarrow CO_2 + H_2O$ (Nothing balanced)

$C_4H_{10} + O_2 \rightarrow 4\ CO_2 + H_2O$ (C is balanced)

$C_4H_{10} + O_2 \rightarrow 4\ CO_2 + 5\ H_2O$ (C and H now balanced)

$C_4H_{10} + 6.5\ O_2 \rightarrow 4\ CO_2 + 5\ H_2O$ (O_2 has decimal coefficient)

$2\ C_4H_{10} + 13\ O_2 \rightarrow 8\ CO_2 + 10\ H_2O$ (Everything balanced, whole numbers)

(b) Octane is an eight-carbon chain: $CH_3CH_2CH_2CH_2CH_2CH_2CH_2CH_3$, C_8H_{18}

$C_8H_{18} + O_2 \rightarrow CO_2 + H_2O$ (Nothing balanced)

$C_8H_{18} + O_2 \rightarrow 8\ CO_2 + H_2O$ (C is balanced)

$C_8H_{18} + O_2 \rightarrow 8\ CO_2 + 9\ H_2O$ (C and H now balanced)

$C_8H_{18} + 12.5\ O_2 \rightarrow 8\ CO_2 + 9\ H_2O$ (O_2 has decimal coefficient)

$2\ C_8H_{18} + 25\ O_2 \rightarrow 16\ CO_2 + 18\ H_2O$ (Everything balanced, whole numbers)

(c) 2-pentene is a five-carbon chain with a double bond after the second carbon:
$CH_3CH=CHCH_2CH_3$, C_5H_{10}

$C_5H_{10} + O_2 \rightarrow CO_2 + H_2O$ (Nothing balanced)

$C_5H_{10} + O_2 \rightarrow 5\ CO_2 + H_2O$ (C is balanced)

$C_5H_{10} + O_2 \rightarrow 5\ CO_2 + 5\ H_2O$ (C and H now balanced)

$C_5H_{10} + 7.5\ O_2 \rightarrow 5\ CO_2 + 5\ H_2O$ (O_2 has decimal coefficient)

$2\ C_5H_{10} + 15\ O_2 \rightarrow 10\ CO_2 + 10\ H_2O$ (Everything balanced, whole numbers)

(d) 1-Hexyne is a six-carbon chain with a triple bond beginning at the first carbon:
$HC{\equiv}CCH_2CH_2CH_2CH_3$, C_6H_{10}

$C_6H_{10} + O_2 \rightarrow CO_2 + H_2O$ (Nothing balanced)

$C_6H_{10} + O_2 \rightarrow 6\ CO_2 + H_2O$ (C is balanced)

$C_6H_{10} + O_2 \rightarrow 6\ CO_2 + 5\ H_2O$ (C and H now balanced)

$C_6H_{10} + 8.5\ O_2 \rightarrow 6\ CO_2 + 5\ H_2O$ (O_2 has decimal coefficient)

$2\ C_6H_{10} + 17\ O_2 \rightarrow 12\ CO_2 + 10\ H_2O$ (Everything balanced, whole numbers)

35.   (a) Propane is a three-carbon chain: $CH_3CH_2CH_3$, C_3H_8

$C_3H_8 + O_2 \rightarrow CO_2 + H_2O$ (Nothing balanced)

$C_3H_8 + O_2 \rightarrow 3\ CO_2 + H_2O$ (C is balanced)

$C_3H_8 + O_2 \rightarrow 3\ CO_2 + 4\ H_2O$ (C and H now balanced)

$C_3H_8 + 5\ O_2 \rightarrow 3\ CO_2 + 4\ H_2O$ (Everything balanced, whole numbers)

(b) Pentane is a five-carbon chain: $CH_3CH_2CH_2CH_2CH_3$, C_5H_{12}

$C_5H_{12} + O_2 \rightarrow CO_2 + H_2O$ (Nothing balanced)

$C_5H_{12} + O_2 \rightarrow 5\ CO_2 + H_2O$ (C is balanced)

$C_5H_{12} + O_2 \rightarrow 5\ CO_2 + 6\ H_2O$ (C and H now balanced)

$C_5H_{12} + 8\ O_2 \rightarrow 5\ CO_2 + 6\ H_2O$ (Everything balanced, whole numbers)

(c) 1-propanol is a five-carbon chain with a double bond after the second carbon:
$HOCH_2CH_2CH_3$, C_3H_7OH

$C_3H_7OH + O_2 \rightarrow CO_2 + H_2O$ (Nothing balanced)

$C_3H_7OH + O_2 \rightarrow 3\ CO_2 + H_2O$ (C is balanced)

$C_3H_7OH + O_2 \rightarrow 3\ CO_2 + 4\ H_2O$ (C and H now balanced)

$C_3H_7OH + 4.5\ O_2 \rightarrow 3\ CO_2 + 4\ H_2O$ (O_2 has decimal coefficient)

$2\ C_3H_7OH + 9\ O_2 \rightarrow 6\ CO_2 + 8\ H_2O$ (Everything balanced, whole numbers)

(d) 1-pentanol is an six-carbon chain with a triple bond beginning at the first carbon:
$HOCH_2CH_2CH_2CH_2CH_3$, $C_5H_{11}OH$

$C_5H_{11}OH + O_2 \rightarrow CO_2 + H_2O$ (Nothing balanced)

$C_5H_{11}OH + O_2 \rightarrow 5\ CO_2 + H_2O$ (C is balanced)

$C_5H_{11}OH + O_2 \rightarrow 5\ CO_2 + 6\ H_2O$ (C and H now balanced)

$C_5H_{11}OH + 7.5\ O_2 \rightarrow 5\ CO_2 + 6\ H_2O$ (O_2 has decimal coefficient)

$$2\ C_5H_{11}OH + 15\ O_2 \rightarrow 10\ CO_2 + 12\ H_2O \qquad \text{(Everything balanced, whole numbers)}$$

37. (a) Al^{3+}, the oxidation number is the same as the charge for a lone atom: +3
    (b) FeO, oxygen is typically −2, so iron must be +2 for the overall neutral charge
    (c) H_2S, hydrogen is typically +1, so sulfur must be −2 for the overall neutral charge
    (d) Fe_3O_2, oxygen is typically −2, so iron must be +3 for the overall neutral charge

39. To determine which element is oxidized and which is reduced, we need to determine the oxidation state of each element in each compound in the reaction:
    (a) $CO_2(g)$: C: +4, O: −2; $H_2O(g)$: H: +1, O: −2;
        $C_6H_{12}O_6(s)$: C: 0, H: +1, O: −2; $O_2(g)$: O: 0
        We can see that carbon goes from +4 to 0 and some of the oxygen goes from −2 to 0. That means that carbon is being reduced and oxygen is being oxidized. Therefore, CO_2 is being reduced and H_2O is being oxidized.
    (b) $CH_4(g)$: C: −4, H: +1; $O_2(g)$: O: 0; $CO_2(g)$: C: +4, O: −2;
        $H_2O(g)$: H: +1, O: −2
        We can see that carbon goes from −4 to +4 and oxygen goes from 0 to −2. That means that carbon is being oxidized and oxygen is being reduced. Therefore, CH_4 is being oxidized and O_2 is being reduced.

41. To determine which element is oxidized and which is reduced, we need to determine the oxidation state of each element in each compound in the reaction:
    (a) CO(g): C: +2, O: −2; $O_2(g)$: O:0; $CO_2(g)$: C: +4, O: −2
        We can see that carbon goes from +2 to +4 and oxygen goes from −2 and 0 to −2. That means that carbon is being oxidized and some of the oxygen is being reduced. Therefore, CO is being oxidized and O_2 is being reduced.
    (b) Na(s): Na: 0; $H_2O(l)$: H: +1, O: −2; NaOH(aq): Na: +1, O: −2, H: +1; $H_2(g)$: H: 0
        We can see that sodium goes from 0 to +1 and hydrogen goes from +1 to +1 and 0. That means that sodium is being oxidized and some of the hydrogen is being reduced. Therefore, Na is being oxidized and H_2O is being reduced.

43. $q = C_p \times M \times \Delta T$
    The problem asks for the specific heat capacity given the mass, heat, and temperature change. Solving for specific heat capacity,
    $C_p = q \div (M \times \Delta T) = 1.00 \times 10^4\ J \div (421\ g \times (49.7°C − 24.7°C)) = 0.950\ J/g·°C$
    (Temperature change is always final temperature minus initial temperature.)

45. $q = C_p \times M \times \Delta T = 1.2\ J/g·°C \times 500.0\ g \times (507°C − 22°C) = 290,000\ J = 290\ kJ$

47. $q = C_p \times M \times \Delta T$
    The problem asks for the mass given the heat, temperature change, and specific heat capacity. Solving for mass,
    $M = q \div (C_p \times \Delta T) = −488\ J \div (0.38\ J/g·°C \times (25°C − 284°C)) = 5.0\ g$
    (The heat is negative because heat was released into the surroundings. Temperature change is always final temperature minus initial temperature.)

49. To solve this problem, we need the density of water. Our textbook says the density of water is 1 g/mL.
    There are 2.00 L of water. $2.00\ L \times (1\ mL / 10^{-3}\ L) \times (1\ g / 1\ mL) = 2000\ g$
    $2000\ g \times 2258\ J/g = 4,520,000\ J = 4.52\ MJ$

51. 152.0 Calories × (1 kcal / 1 Cal) × (10^3 cal / 1 kcal) × (4.184 J / 1 cal) = 636,000 J
     636,000 J ÷ 2258 J/g = 282 g
     Using the density of water given in our textbook (1 g/mL),
     282 g × (1 mL / 1 g) = 282 mL = 0.282 L of water

53. First, heat must be used to raise the temperature of the copper to its melting point:
     q = C_p × M × ΔT = 0.38 J/g·°C × 84.4 g × (1082°C − 25°C) = 34,000 J
     Then, heat must be used to melt the copper:
     84.4 g × 207 J/g = 17,000 J
     The total heat is:
     34,000 J + 17,000 J = 51,000 J = 5.1 × 10^5 J

55.

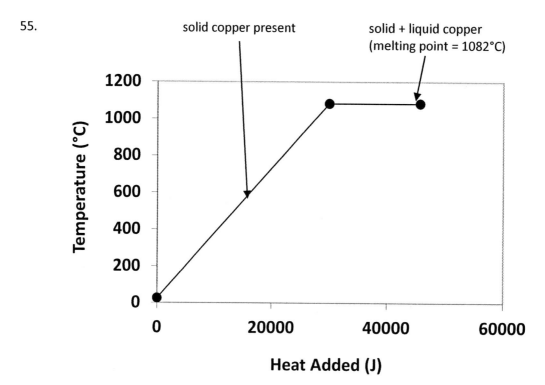

solid copper present   solid + liquid copper
                                (melting point = 1082°C)

57. q_{water} = −q_{metal}
     $C_{p\ water}$ × m_{water} × ΔT_{water} = − $C_{p\ metal}$ × m_{metal} × ΔT_{metal}
     $C_{p\ metal}$ = − ($C_{p\ water}$ × m_{water} × ΔT_{water}) ÷ (m_{metal} × ΔT_{metal})
     $C_{p\ metal}$ = − (4.184 J/g·°C × 100.0 g × (25.3°C − 21.2°C)) ÷ (15.6 g × (25.3°C − 225°C))
     $C_{p\ metal}$ = 0.551 J/g·°C

59. q_{water} = −q_{metal}
     $C_{p\ water}$ × m_{water} × ΔT_{water} = − $C_{p\ metal}$ × m_{metal} × ΔT_{metal}
     ΔT_{metal} = − ($C_{p\ water}$ × m_{water} × ΔT_{water}) ÷ ($C_{p\ metal}$ × m_{metal})
     $T_{f(metal)}$ − $T_{i(metal)}$ = − ($C_{p\ water}$ × m_{water} × ΔT_{water}) ÷ ($C_{p\ metal}$ × m_{metal})
     $T_{i(metal)}$ = $T_{f(metal)}$ + ($C_{p\ water}$ × m_{water} × ΔT_{water}) ÷ ($C_{p\ metal}$ × m_{metal})
     $T_{i(metal)}$ = 34.1°C + (4.184 J/g·°C × 50.0 g × (34.1°C − 20.3°C)) ÷ (0.38 J/g·°C × 24.9 g)
     $T_{i(metal)}$ = 339.2°C

61.   This problem requires an application of the first law of thermodynamics. The heat lost through the combustion of the Teflon must be equal to the heat gained by the water. Since we know the mass and temperature for the water (we also know the specific heat capacity, which is 4.184 J/g·°C), we can calculate the heat gained by the water:

$q = C_p \times M \times \Delta T = 4.184$ J/g·°C $\times$ 1,000.0 g $\times$ (35.8°C − 25.5°C) = 43,100 J

Because of the first law of thermodynamics, the heat gained by the water must be equal to the heat lost by the combustion of Teflon. This means that q for the Teflon must be −43,100 J (since heat was lost, q is negative).

Since we know the heat of combustion of the Teflon, we can now calculate the number of grams of Teflon that were consumed:

−43,100 J ÷ −5 × 10^3 J/g = 8.62 g Teflon consumed

63. $q_{combustion} = -q_{calorimeter}$
−1.97 x 10^4 J/g x 1.20 g = −4.184 J/g·°C x 500.0 g x ΔT
$\Delta T = 11.3$°C
$\Delta T = T_f - T_i$
$T_f = \Delta T + T_i$
$T_f = 11.3$°C + 25.0°C = 36.3°C

65.   This problem also requires an application of the first law of thermodynamics. The heat lost through the combustion of the flammable fuel must be equal to the heat gained by the water. Since we know the mass and temperature for the water (we also know the specific heat capacity, which is 4.184 J/g·°C), we can calculate the heat gained by the water (1.00 L of water has a mass of 1.00 kg according to the density of water: 1 g/mL):

$q = C_p \times M \times \Delta T = 4.184$ J/g·°C $\times$ 1,000 g $\times$ (31.2°C − 26.8°C) = 18409.6 J ≈ 18,400 J

Because of the first law of thermodynamics, the heat gained by the water must be equal to the heat lost by the combustion of flammable fuel. This means that q for the fuel must be −18,400 J (since heat was lost, q is negative).

Since we know the mass of the fuel, we can now calculate the heat of combustion:

−18,400 J ÷ 3.35 g = −55,000 J/g = −5.50 × 10^5 J/g

The heat of combustion is 5.50 × 10^5 J/g

67.   In a fire sprinkler, a solid plug should have a melting temperature that allows it to melt at temperatures typically reached in a fire but not during normal building operation. The liquid in a vial should have a boiling temperature that allows it to boil and shatter the vial in a fire but not in normal conditions.

69.   If benzene is found in a blank sample of carpeting that has been analyzed by gas chromatography, the only way the presence of benzene in the suspected sample could still be used to determine if an accelerant was used to ignite the fire is if there is significantly more benzene in the suspected sample than in the blank. Even still, it would be difficult for a jury to accept that evidence "beyond reasonable doubt."

71.   If signs of electrical arcing are present in an electrical box, that does not necessarily prove that a structural fire was caused by the arcing. There also must be sufficient evidence to show that the electrical box was the source of the fire.

73. Smoke consists of small particles freed from materials burning in a fire. If flames appear to be forming out of the smoke that is pouring out of a structural fire, that could be entirely possible. If the temperature of the smoke is high enough, the exposure of the smoke to the oxygen-enriched atmosphere outside the structure could allow the particles that make up the smoke to burst into flames once they reach open air.

75. No; cone calorimeters are measuring the decrease of oxygen when being used up in the combustion reaction, so the values will be a bit different.

77. If a large amount of heated smoke is trapped near the ceiling, it is entirely possible that a plastic fire detector might melt during a fire even if it had never been tampered with.

79. Fire requires fuel, heat, and oxygen to burn. Charring between deck boards can easily result if the deck boards are sufficiently close together to limit the amount of oxygen. The charring would take place because there is insufficient oxygen present for complete combustion.

Chapter 10

Chemistry of Explosions

1. For a compound to be explosive, it must be capable of releasing a large amount of energy. In addition, the compound must react instantaneously and release substantial amounts of gaseous products.

3. According to our textbook, most low explosives serve as propellants for guns and military artillery.

5. It is important for explosive molecules to contain C, H, and O because they have gaseous combustion products (carbon dioxide and water) and the compound already contains some (if not all) of the oxygen necessary to produce those products. This makes them easier to oxidize than a pure hydrocarbon (due to their oxygen balance).

7. The four premises, according to our textbook, are:
   1. Gas particles are extremely small and have relatively large distances between them.
   2. Gas particles act independently of one another; there are no attractive or repulsive forces between gas particles.
   3. Gas particles are continuously moving in random, straight-line motion as they collide with each other and the container walls.
   4. The average kinetic energy of gas particles is proportional to the temperature of the gas.

9. Gases can be compressed to a much greater extent than liquids and solids because they have much more space between their particles (see premise #1 of kinetic molecular theory).

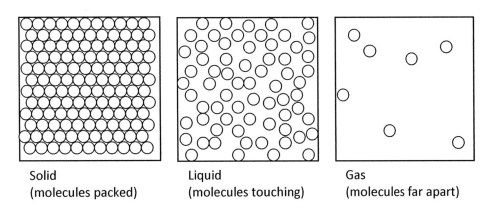

| Solid
(molecules packed) | Liquid
(molecules touching) | Gas
(molecules far apart) |

11. Above the UEL (upper explosive limit), the fuel-air mixture is too fuel-rich for the fuel to react explosively because the reaction is limited by the amount of oxygen present in the mixture.

13. Avogadro's law says that volume is directly proportional to the number of gas particles if temperature and pressure are held constant. As the number of particles increases, the volume of gas increases. As the number of particles decreases, the volume of gas decreases.

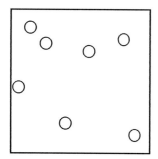 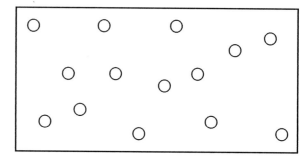

If we double the number of gas molecules, we also double the volume of gas present.

15. Gay-Lussac's law says that pressure is directly proportional to temperature if volume and number of moles are held constant. As the temperature increases, the pressure increases. As the temperature decreases, the pressure decreases.

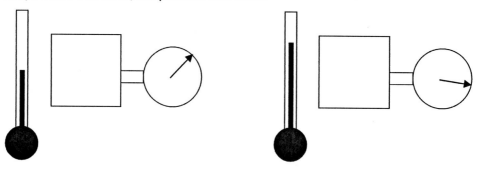

As the temperature increases, the pressure inside the gas chamber increases.

17. STP is an abbreviation for standard temperature and pressure. These are the conditions of 1 atm pressure (760 mmHg, 760 torr, 101.325 kPa) and 273.15 K (0°C, 32°F).

19. Dalton's law of partial pressures states that the total pressure of a gas mixture is the sum of the pressures of each component in the mixture. This requires that each gas behaves independently of all other gases in the mixture and each gas continues to undergo collisions in the same exact manner. This is consistent with the four premises of the kinetic molecular theory of gases (see answer to #7 above). Premise #2 is most applicable, saying that the gas particles act independently of one another. If particles of one gas act independently of other particles of the same gas, it is a natural extension to say that particles of one gas act independently of particles of a second gas.

21. Chemical markers are high vapor pressure compounds that are included in plastic explosives by their manufacturers. The high vapor pressure compound forms a vapor surrounding the plastic explosive that is more easily detected than the explosive itself. As a result, it is easier to detect the explosives (using canine or electronic detection systems) and prevent their illegal use.

23. Taggants, markers, and isomers help security officials during all phases of explosive detection and identification. Chemical markers enable security officials to detect explosives before they are used. Taggants and isomers allow the identification of an explosive either before or after detonation. This helps the security officials track the explosive from factory through sale to use and identify any illegal activity along the way.

25. The most straightforward way to determine the number of moles of oxygen required for the complete oxidation of a compound to CO_2 and H_2O is to balance the chemical equation. If we balance the carbon, hydrogen, and oxygen but do not convert the coefficients to whole numbers, we can simply look at the coefficient on O_2 to answer the question.
    (a) $CH_3CH_3 + 3.5\ O_2 \rightarrow 2\ CO_2 + 3\ H_2O$ 3.5 moles O_2 required
    (b) $CH_3CH_2CH_2CH_3 + 6.5\ O_2 \rightarrow 4\ CO_2 + 5\ H_2O$ 6.5 moles O_2 required
    (c) $CH_2{=}CH_2 + 3\ O_2 \rightarrow 2\ CO_2 + 2\ H_2O$ 3 moles O_2 required
    (d) $CH_3CH_2OH + 3\ O_2 \rightarrow 2\ CO_2 + 3\ H_2O$ 3 moles O_2 required

27. This problem is the same as #25, but with the added step of knowing the formula given the name.
    (a) ethane (CH_3CH_3, C_2H_6): $C_2H_6 + 3.5\ O_2 \rightarrow 2\ CO_2 + 3\ H_2O$ 3.5 moles O_2 required
    (b) ethanol (CH_3CH_2OH, C_2H_5OH): $C_2H_5OH + 3\ O_2 \rightarrow 2\ CO_2 + 3\ H_2O$ 3 moles O_2 required
    (c) butane ($CH_3CH_2CH_2CH_3$, C_4H_{10}): $C_4H_{10} + 6.5\ O_2 \rightarrow 4\ CO_2 + 5\ H_2O$ 6.5 moles O_2 required
    (d) propene ($CH_2{=}CHCH_3$, C_3H_6): $C_3H_6 + 4.5\ O_2 \rightarrow 3\ CO_2 + 3\ H_2O$ 4.5 moles O_2 required

29. (a) If volume decreases, pressure increases (Boyle's Law).
    (b) If temperature increases, volume increases (Charles's Law).
    (c) If temperature decreases, pressure decreases (Gay-Lussac's Law).
    (d) If the amount of gas decreases, pressure decreases (Avogadro's Law).

31. Avogadro's law can be written: $n_1 \div V_1 = n_2 \div V_2$.
    (a) $n_2 = (n_1 \div V_1) \times V_2 = (0.651\ mol \div 2.00\ L) \times 0.575\ L = 0.187\ mol$
    (b) $V_1 = (V_2 \div n_2) \times n_1 = (750.0\ mL \div 1.25\ mol) \times 1.36\ mol = 816\ L$
    (c) $V_2 = (V_1 \div n_1) \times n_2 = (0.334\ L \div 0.521\ mol) \times 6.77\ mol = 4.34\ L$
    (d) $n_2 = (n_1 \div V_1) \times V_2 = (4.71\ mol \div 17.2\ L) \times 5.86\ L = 1.60\ mol$

33. Boyle's law can be written: $P_1 \times V_1 = P_2 \times V_2$
    (a) $P_2 = P_1 \times V_1 \div V_2 = 5.44\ atm \times 3.74\ L \div 6.64\ L = 3.06\ atm$
    (b) $V_2 = P_1 \times V_1 \div P_2 = 0.177\ atm \times 0.565\ L \div 4.71\ atm = 0.0212\ L$
    (c) $V_1 = P_2 \times V_2 \div P_1 = 4.28\ atm \times 0.904\ L \div 6.03\ atm = 4.90\ L$
    (d) $P_1 = P_2 \times V_2 \div V_1 = 5.47\ atm \times 2.85\ L \div 7.43\ L = 2.10\ atm$

35. Gay-Lussac's law can be written: $P_1 \div T_1 = P_2 \div T_2$.
    (a) $T_2 = (T_1 \div P_1) \times P_2 = (300.0\ K \div 1.02\ atm) \times 7.48\ atm = 2200\ K$
    (b) $P_1 = (P_2 \div T_2) \times T_1 = (8.54\ atm \div 607\ K) \times 266\ K = 3.74\ atm$
    (c) $T_1 = (T_2 \div P_2) \times P_1 = (279\ K \div 3.47\ atm) \times 5.74\ atm = 462\ K$
    (d) $P_2 = (P_1 \div T_1) \times T_2 = (6.16\ atm \div 287\ K) \times 484\ K = 10.4\ atm$

37. Charles's law can be written: $V_1 \div T_1 = V_2 \div T_2$.
    (a) $T_2 = (T_1 \div V_1) \times V_2 = (379\ K \div 1.25\ L) \times 9.92\ L = 3010\ K$
    (b) $V_1 = (V_2 \div T_2) \times T_1 = (28.3\ L \div 612\ K) \times 118\ K = 5.46\ L$
    (c) $V_1 = (V_2 \div T_2) \times T_1 = (5.76\ L \div 828\ K) \times 298\ K = 2.07\ L$
    (d) $T_2 = (T_1 \div V_1) \times V_2 = (318\ K \div 6.11\ L) \times 6.83\ L = 355\ K$

39. At STP, 1 mol of gas has volume 22.4 L. Using Avogadro's law,
$V_2 = (V_1 \div n_1) \times n_2 = (22.4 \text{ L} \div 1 \text{ mol}) \times n_2 = 22.4 \text{ L/mol} \times n_2$
(a) 22.4 L/mol × 5.72 mol = 140. L
(b) 22.4 L/mol × 21.1 mol = 515 L
(c) 22.4 L/mol × 0.682 mol = 16.6 L
(d) 22.4 L/mol × 0.744 mol = 18.2 L

41. At STP, 1 mol of gas has volume 22.4 L. Using Avogadro's law,
$V_2 = (V_1 \div n_1) \times n_2 = (22.4 \text{ L} \div 1 \text{ mol}) \times n_2 = 22.4 \text{ L/mol} \times n_2$. First, we need to determine the number of moles of gas using the molar mass.
(a) 6.57 g methane ÷ (12.0115 g/mol C + 4 × (1.00794 g/mol H)) = 0.410 mol
22.4 L/mol × 0.410 mol = 10.0 L
(b) 3.68 g oxygen ÷ (2 × (15.9994 g/mol O)) = 0.115 mol
22.4 L/mol × 0.115 mol = 2.81 L
(c) 52.2 g carbon monoxide ÷ (12.0115 g/mol C + 15.9994 g/mol O) = 1.86 mol
22.4 L/mol × 1.86 mol = 45.6 L
(d) 48.6 g dinitrogen monoxide ÷ (2 × (14.0067 g/mol N) + 15.9994 g/mol O) = 1.10 mol
22.4 L/mol × 1.10 mol = 26.8 L

43. Density is calculated using the equation $D = m \div V$.
(a) D = 6.57 g ÷ 10.0 L = 0.657 g/L
(b) D = 3.68 g ÷ 2.81 L = 1.31 g/L
(c) D = 52.2 g ÷ 45.6 L = 1.14 g/L
(d) D = 48.6 g ÷ 26.8 L = 1.81 g/L

45. Since we are given volume, temperature, and pressure and temperature and pressure change, the simplest way to approach this problem is using the combined gas law:
$P_1 \times V_1 \div T_1 = P_2 \times V_2 \div T_2$
The only requirement is that temperature is in absolute temperature units, so we need to convert the temperatures to Kelvin.
25°C = 298 K, 175°C = 448 K
Solving for V_2, $V_2 = (P_1 \times V_1 \times T_2) \div (T_1 \times P_2)$
V_2 = (3.00 atm × 2.00 L × 448 K) ÷ (298 K × 1.00 atm) = 9.02 L

47. $P_1 V_1 / T_1 = P_2 V_2 / T_2$; (1.10 atm) (12.0 L) / (301.5 K) = (0.625 atm) (18.7 L) / T_2;
T_2 = 266 K = –6°C

49. Since we are only given one set of conditions, this is an opportunity to use the ideal gas law.
$P \times V = n \times R \times T$, where R = 0.08206 L atm/mol K.
Solving for P, $P = n \times R \times T \div V$
P = 32.4 mol × 0.08206 L atm/mol K × 357 K ÷ 18.0 L = 52.7 atm

51. Again using the ideal gas law, but this time solving for V, $V = n \times R \times T \div P$. First we need to calculate the number of moles of gas present. Temperature must also be converted to Kelvin:
22.7°C = 295.9 K
2547 g butane ÷ (4 × (12.0115 g/mol C) + 10 × (1.00794 g/mol H)) = 43.82 mol C_4H_{10}
V = 43.82 mol × 0.08206 L atm/mol K × 295.9 K ÷ 56.4 atm = 18.87 L

53. Again using the ideal gas law, but this time solving for T,
$T = (P \times V) \div (n \times R)$

T = (38.1 atm × 875 L) ÷ (64.1 mol × 0.08206 L atm/mol K) = 6340 K = 6060 °C

55. $n = PV / RT$
      n = (14.4 atm × 12.0 L) / (0.08206 L atm/mol K × 298.3 K) = 7.06 mol

57. $P = nRT / V$
      72.3 g CO_2 ÷ 44.009 g/mol CO_2 = 1.64 mol CO_2
      P = (1.64 mol × 0.08206 L atm/mol K × 294.6 K) / 5.45 L = 7.29 atm

59. $n = PV / RT$
      n = (3.20 atm × 0.0750 L) / (0.08206 L atm/mol K × 293.2 K) = 0.0099750657 mol ≈ 0.00998 mol
      0.201 g ÷ 0.00998 mol = 20.1 g/mol
      The noble gas is neon (Ne, atomic mass 20.180 g/mol)

61. $n = PV / RT$
      n = (0.980 atm × 65.0 L) / (0.08206 L atm/mol K × 293.2 K) = 2.65 mol
      2.65 mol N_2 × (2 mol NaN_3 / 3 mol N_2) = 1.77 mol NaN_3
      1.77 mol NaN_3 × 65.011 g/mol NaN_3 = 115 g NaN_3

63.   The problem tells us how it needs to be solved: Dalton's law of partial pressures and the ideal gas law. There are two possible approaches to the problem: determine the partial pressures of O_2 and N_2 and add them to get the total pressure, or determine the total moles of gas and calculate the total pressure. We will use the second approach.
      16.0 g O_2 ÷ (2×15.9994 g/mol O) = 0.500 mol
      28.0 g N_2 ÷ (2×14.0067 g/mol N) = 1.00 mol
      The total number of moles is 0.500 mol + 1.00 mol = 1.50 mol.
      Solving the ideal gas law for pressure, $P = n × R × T ÷ V$
      P = 1.50 mol × 0.08206 L atm/mol K × 298 K ÷ 1.00 L = 36.7 atm

65.   To determine the oxygen balance, we need to obtain the balanced chemical equation for the combustion or decomposition reaction:
      $C_4H_8N_8O_8$ + 2 O_2 → 4 CO_2 + 4 H_2O + 4 N_2
      Since HMX requires additional oxygen to undergo complete combustion, it has a negative oxygen balance.

67.   Explosives with a positive oxygen balance will produce white smoke because the major component will be steam condensing on the small particles produced by the explosion. Explosives with a negative oxygen balance will produce black, sooty smoke because there will be partially combusted particles composed primarily of leftover carbon.

69.   Gases are in constant, random motion and collide with other gas molecules. An explosion requires that the fuel, oxygen, and ignition source are present simultaneously. If the partial pressure of fuel is below the LEL, an explosion will not occur; if it is above the UEL, there is insufficient oxygen for the reaction to continue. Because fuels are in constant random motion, a fuel initially present at a partial pressure above the UEL may soon become explosive as the fuel mixes with oxygen gas from the environment, thus lowering its partial pressure.

71.   For proper breathing, a person's lungs must be able to expand and contract (via diaphragm movements) to create a pressure difference with respect to the outside atmosphere. To inhale, the lungs expand (increase V, decreasing P), thereby reducing the pressure of the air in

the lungs, drawing in outside air. In order to exhale, the lungs contract (decrease V, increasing P), increasing the pressure of the air in the lungs and forcing some outside of the body. If a puncture wound is suffered, then the lungs have great difficulty creating a pressure difference and it is very hard to breath.

73.   The isomers of DNT are: 2,3-dinitrotoluene; 2,4-dinitrotoluene, 2,5-dinitrotoluene, 2,6-dinitrotoluene, 3,4-dinitrotoluene, and 3,5-dinitrotoluene.

2,3-dinitrotoluene   2,4-dinitrotoluene   3,4-dinitrotoluene

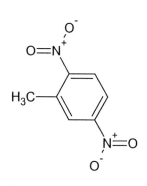

2,5-dinitrotoluene   2,6-dinitrotoluene   3,5-dinitrotoluene

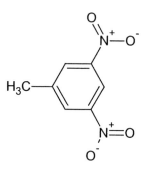

75. $4\ C_3H_5N_3O_9(l) \rightarrow 12\ CO_2(g) + 10\ H_2O(g) + 6\ N_2(g) + O_2(g)$
100.0 g nitroglycerine ÷ 228.0924 g/mol nitroglycerine = 0.4384 mol $C_3H_6N_3O_9$
0.4384 mol $C_3H_6N_3O_9$ × (12 mol CO_2 / 4 mol $C_3H_6N_3O_9$) = 1.315 mol CO_2
0.4384 mol $C_3H_6N_3O_9$ × (10 mol H_2O / 4 mol $C_3H_6N_3O_9$) = 1.096 mol H_2O
0.4384 mol $C_3H_6N_3O_9$ × (6 mol N_2 / 4 mol $C_3H_6N_3O_9$) = 0.6576 mol N_2
0.4384 mol $C_3H_6N_3O_9$ × (1 mol O_2 / 4 mol $C_3H_6N_3O_9$) = 0.1096 mol O_2
$P = nRT\ /\ V$
P_{CO_2} = 1.315 mol × 0.08206 L atm/mol K × 773.2 K ÷ 23.0 L = 3.628 atm CO_2
P_{H_2O} = 1.096 mol × 0.08206 L atm/mol K × 773.2 K ÷ 23.0 L = 3.023 atm H_2O
P_{N_2} = 0.6576 mol × 0.08206 L atm/mol K × 773.2 K ÷ 23.0 L = 1.814 atm N_2
P_{O_2} = 0.1096 mol × 0.08206 L atm/mol K × 773.2 K ÷ 23.0 L = 0.3023 atm O_2
$P_{total} = P_{CO_2} + P_{H_2O} + P_{N_2} + P_{O_2}$ = 8.767 atm

77.   Since explosives are used so frequently and in such large quantities, taggants will be spread to such an extent that it would be very difficult to differentiate taggants already in the

environments from the ones that might be able to indicate the presence of an explosive device at a crime scene.

79.   The second TLC plate shows the best separation of all five explosive components, although TNT and PETN are very difficult to distinguish. The first plate does not adequately separate the TNT, PETN, and NG components from each other. The third plate does not adequately separate the RDX and tetryl components from each other.

81.   If the explosion had ruptured the cabin integrity at high altitude, the higher pressure inside the cabin than surrounding the airplane would have caused the air to rush out through the rupture, depressurizing the entire airplane.

Chapter 11

Applications of Chemical Kinetics

1. The rates of chemical reactions are very important to understand when trying to establish evidence of time in forensic science. Our textbook opens this chapter talking about the case of "Kari" in the Hawaiian islands. In that case, a forensic etymologist was able to use his knowledge about the rate of growth of insects and their feeding habits to more accurately estimate the time of death for the victim. Knowing the rates of other chemical reactions can give similar sorts of information.

3. According to our textbook, the three principles of collision theory are:
    1. The reactants must collide for a reaction to take place.
    2. Collisions must have high energy.
    3. The colliding particles must be properly oriented for a reaction to occur.

5. The initial concentration of the reactants affects most reaction rates because they determine the number of collisions that can potentially take place between reactant molecules. According to collision theory, reactants must collide for a reaction to take place. Therefore, the initial concentration will often have an effect on reaction rates.

7. Bloody clothes recovered as evidence are immediately dried because the moisture in the clothes is a reactant in the decomposition reactions of the blood. If the clothes are dry, the biological evidence degrades more slowly, and more information can be obtained by the forensic scientists.

9. It is not enough simply for the molecules to have sufficient energy. The collisions must also have the correct orientation for a reaction to take place. As a result, only a fraction of collisions between molecules having sufficient energy will result in the reaction of the reactant molecules.

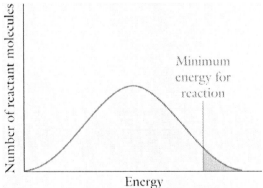

The shaded portion indicates the fraction of reactant molecules that have sufficient energy to react.

11.   Increasing the temperature of a reaction system does not change the amount of energy needed for reactants to cross the activation barrier. As the temperature increases, the average kinetic energy of the molecules increases. This causes the collisions to have greater energy and allows the reaction to occur more quickly.

13.   The greater the surface area of a heterogeneous catalyst, the more available reaction sites on the surface of the catalyst. Since reaction rate depends on the number of collisions that take place, having more available reaction sites on the surface increases the rate of the reaction.

15.   Adding a catalyst is the only method of increasing the reaction rate that works by lowering the activation energy. The catalyst provides an alternative pathway (mechanism) for the reaction to take place, which is lower in energy than the pathway for the uncatalyzed reaction.

17.   A catalytic converter is a heterogeneous catalyst. Solid particles are suspended on a porous support to maximize surface area, and the reactants pass over the catalyst in the gas phase.

19.   Most enzyme catalyzed reactions have zero-order kinetics. Doubling the concentration of the enzyme will not have any effect on the rate of the reaction. However, at some point, the enzyme molecules impede the mixing and collision of reactant molecules, so the rate will eventually decrease. Since a very small amount of enzyme is required to catalyze the reaction, this is a highly unusual situation.

21.   The analysis of blood alcohol can be done hours after a person has been detained, and an accurate value for the BAC can be determined as of the time a person was arrested. The method for this analysis relies on knowing the rate of oxidation of ethanol to carbon dioxide in the body.

23.   If an investigator determines the blood serum levels of both legal and illegal drugs, he or she can use this information coupled with the half-lives of those drugs to estimate the blood serum level of those drugs at some earlier time (such as when the drugs were originally taken into the body). This can help predict the level of intoxication and determine whether a drug could have been the cause of death for a victim.

25.   After 16 hrs, 0.469 mg remains out of a 30 mg dose. We can estimate the half-life by determining how many half-lives have passed:
30 mg → 15 mg → 7.5 mg → 3.75 mg → 1.875 mg → 0.9375 mg → 0.46875 mg ≈ 0.469 mg
Therefore, six half-lives have passed in 16 hours. That means the half-life of the pharmaceutical is 16 hrs ÷ 6 = 2.67 hrs = 160 minutes.

27.   The injured person claims the headlights were out at the time of the accident, while the driver claims that the broken headlight resulted from the accident. The key lies in the rate of oxidation of the filament. If the headlights were on at the time of the accident, the filament would be at 3000 K as the headlight broke. This would result in the rapid oxidation of the filament. If it was off, it would be at a much lower temperature (approximately 300 K is a normal temperature) and the rate of oxidation would be much slower and less oxidized material would be present. If the headlight broke at a different time (before the accident), there are two possibilities: either the headlight was on, or it was off. In either case, the same oxidation processes would take place, but there would be additional oxidation over the time between the break and the accident. The investigator would need to carefully measure the amount of oxidized material and compare it to the amount of oxidized material in headlights of the same make and model that are tested in a controlled environment. Then the courts can determine who is telling the truth about the headlights.

29.   Hair analysis would work best for long-term use of illegal drugs (provided the hair is long enough) because drug metabolites are stored in the hair shaft over a period of time. Blood/urine testing would work best for recent illegal drug use (<2 weeks) because drug metabolites can be found within those fluids during a short period of time after drug use.

31.   The missing person was reported on February 25 and the body was located on March 21. This is early spring in northern California, so insects are not as active as they would be during a warmer time of year. This would delay the rate of insect activity in the body and give an estimated time of death that is different from that given by other procedures.

33.   Lead-210 would not work well for a recent homicide victim because its relatively long half-life of 22.3 years. Similarly, polonium-210 would not work on an older homicide because its half-life is only 138 days. If the victim was found buried 30 years after having disappeared, essentially all of the polonium-210 would have decayed and the time since death could not be determined.

Chapter 12

Nuclear Chemistry:
Energy, Medicine, Weapons, and Terrorism

1. Henri Becquerel originally thought that phosphorescence was related to X-rays. He used a mineral crystal containing salts of uranium on a wrapped photographic plate. When the mineral crystal was exposed to sunlight and then put in the dark, it exhibited phosphorescence and exposed the photographic plate. By chance, he did the same experiment with a crystal that had not been exposed to sunlight (it was left in a drawer). He discovered that the same pattern of exposure was present on the photographic plate. Clearly, the X-rays were resulting from something other than phosphorescence. The mineral crystal was phosphorescent, but it also emitted X-rays in the absence of exposure to sunlight. This eventually led to the discovery of radioactivity.

3. If Becquerel had used a mineral ore other than one that contained uranium, it is likely that he would not have discovered radioactivity. He would have found that phosphorescent materials do not emit X-rays and would have tried to find another way to explain that phenomenon, altogether missing the opportunity to shape history by the accidental discovery of the radioactivity of uranium.

5. Neutrons help to stabilize the nucleus of the atom. Since protons have positive charge, they repel one another. The neutrons can be thought of as the "glue" holding the nucleus together, according to our textbook.

7. Alpha decay is the emission of an alpha particle (a helium nucleus). As a result, the atomic mass decreases by four atomic mass units. The nucleus loses two protons and two neutrons. Beta decay is the emission of a beta particle (an electron). As a result, the atomic mass decreases by a very small amount (less than 0.001 atomic mass units). The number of neutrons decreases by one and the number of protons (and the atomic number) increases by one. Gamma particles have no mass, so gamma emission has no effect on the atomic mass or atomic number of the atom.

9. Alpha particles have the greatest ionization power (because they have a +2 charge). Gamma particles have the least ionization power (because they have no charge).

11. Inside the body, alpha particles pose the greatest risk. This is because they have the greatest ionization power and can damage the tissues as a result. They also have the least penetrating power, so they remain in the body until they have impacted a large amount of tissue. Gamma particles have a higher energy, but they have a great penetrating power and will leave the body before doing too much damage.

13. According to our textbook, balancing a nuclear equation is based on the law of conservation of mass. The total mass of protons and neutrons on each side of the equation is conserved, not the identity of the elements.

15.   The longer the half-life, the more stable the nucleus. A more stable nucleus will take longer to decay, so its half-life will be longer.

17.   Radioisotopes used for medical diagnosis should have an affinity for a particular organ or target a specific system within the body that is being analyzed. They should also be short-lived within the body and have minimal ionization power. Radioisotopes used for cancer treatment should also have an affinity for a particular organ or target a specific system within the body. They should also be short-lived within the body and should have minimal penetration power to limit the damage done to organs or systems not intended to receive the treatment.

19.   Carbon-14 atoms are produced when cosmic rays interact with nitrogen-14 atoms in the atmosphere. The resulting carbon-14 atoms react with atmospheric oxygen to produce carbon dioxide, and this carbon dioxide is taken up by plants during photosynthesis to produce sugars. These are then eaten by animals. As living things continually take in nutrients, the level of carbon-14 in living tissue reaches a steady state.

21.   As described in the figure caption for Figure 12.4 (below), uranium fuel rods release large amounts of heat while undergoing fission reactions in the reactor core. The heat from the reactor core is used to convert water into steam, which is used to turn a steam turbine that generates the electricity. The steam is then cooled and converted back into liquid water by fresh water pumped in from a lake or river. The freshwater is then cooled in the cooling towers before it is returned to the lake or river.

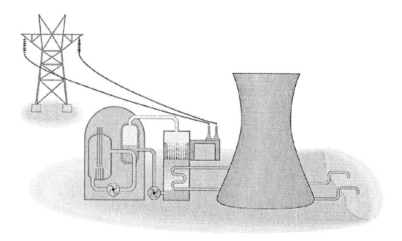

(Illustration adapted from HowStuffWorks.com)

23. A nuclear chain reaction occurs when a fission reaction generates multiple small particles (often neutrons) that in turn initiate more fission reactions. Control rods are used in a nuclear power plant to absorb excess neutrons produced in the fission reaction to avoid a chain reaction. The figure below is taken from Figure 12.9 of the textbook.

$$\,^{1}_{0}n \;+\; ^{235}_{92}U \;\longrightarrow\; ^{91}_{56}Ba \;+\; ^{142}_{36}Kr \;+\; 3\,^{1}_{0}n$$

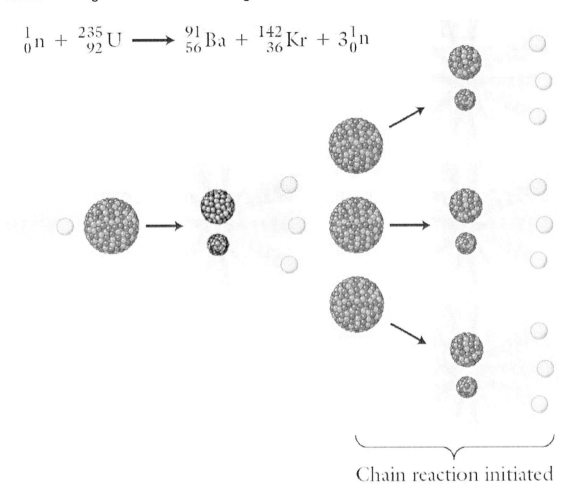

Chain reaction initiated

25. Enriched uranium has a higher percentage of radioactive 235U. Depleted uranium has a higher percentage of less radioactive 238U. Enriched uranium is used for nuclear fuel rods and nuclear fission weapons. Depleted uranium is used as a high density metal in projectile weapons.

27. It is desirable to have nondestructive analysis of samples in forensic science because that leaves open the possibility of analyzing the sample using another technique at a later date. If a destructive technique is used, the sample is lost after that analysis takes place and no subsequent techniques can be used. This makes neutron activation analysis (NAA) advantageous.

29. It is supposed to be used for demoralizing the public by hitting a target that has economic, historic, psychological or political importance. The scientific issues involved deal primarily with the clean-up process: How can you do it cheaper and faster and get rid of all radioactive substances?

31.   Underground testing of nuclear weapons is a safer alternative to above-ground testing because there is less chance that radioactive isotopes will be vaporized and dispersed into the atmosphere. Below ground, the radioactive isotopes are better contained and (theoretically) the long-term impacts of the detonation can be minimized.

33.   To balance a radioactive decay system, we need to balance the number of protons (through looking at atomic number) and the number of neutrons (through looking at atomic mass). Alpha decay produces an alpha particle, $^{4}_{2}$He. Beta decay produces a beta particle, $^{0}_{-1}$e.

(a) $^{239}_{92}$U $\rightarrow$ $^{239}_{93}$Np $+$ $^{0}_{-1}$e

(b) $^{210}_{84}$Po $\rightarrow$ $^{206}_{82}$Pb $+$ $^{4}_{2}$He

(c) $^{90}_{38}$Sr $\rightarrow$ $^{90}_{39}$Y $+$ $^{0}_{-1}$e

(d) $^{174}_{79}$Au $\rightarrow$ $^{170}_{77}$Ir $+$ $^{4}_{2}$He

35.   To balance a radioactive decay system, we need to balance the number of protons (through looking at atomic number) and the number of neutrons (through looking at atomic mass).

(a) $^{198}_{79}$Au $\rightarrow$ $^{0}_{-1}$e $+$ $\mathbf{^{198}_{80}Hg}$

(b) $^{137}_{55}$Cs $\rightarrow$ $^{0}_{-1}\mathbf{e}$ $+$ $^{137}_{56}$Ba

(c) $^{232}_{90}$Th $\rightarrow$ $^{4}_{2}\mathbf{He}$ $+$ $^{228}_{88}$Ra

(d) $^{42}_{19}$K $\rightarrow$ $^{0}_{-1}$e $+$ $^{42}_{20}\mathbf{Ca}$

37.   (a) 31.3 g of iodine-131 remain after four half lives. Originally, there would have been 2^4 = 16 times as much iodine-131 present, or 501 g ^{131}I present.

(b) According to Table 12.1, the half-life of iodine-131 is 8.0 days. 40.0 days is equivalent to five half-lives. If 4.62 kg remain after five half-lives, then 2^5 = 32 times as much iodine-131 was initially present, or 148 kg ^{131}I initially.

(c) 47.1 mg of einsteinium-243 undergo three half-lives, so $(1/2)^3$ = 1/8 as much einsteinium will remain. Therefore, 5.89 mg of ^{243}Es will remain.

(d) According to Table 12.1, the half-life of einsteinium-243 is 21 s. 105 s is equivalent to five half-lives. If 0.147 g were initially present, then $(1/2)^5$ = 1/32 as much einsteinium-243 will remain, or 0.00459 g ^{243}Es will remain.

39.   To balance a radioactive decay system, we need to balance the number of protons (through looking at atomic number) and the number of neutrons (through looking at atomic mass).

(a) $^{57}_{27}\mathbf{Co}$ $+$ $^{0}_{-1}$e $\rightarrow$ $^{57}_{26}$Fe $+$ γ

(b) $^{59}_{27}\mathbf{Co}$ $+$ $^{1}_{0}$n $\rightarrow$ $^{60}_{27}$Co $+$ γ

(c) $^{111}_{50}\mathbf{Sn}$ $+$ $^{0}_{-1}$e $\rightarrow$ $^{111}_{49}\mathbf{In}$

(d) $^{32}_{16}\mathbf{S}$ $+$ $^{4}_{2}$He $\rightarrow$ $^{36}_{18}$Ar

41.   Hair grows slowly and is made from waste protein and other compounds from within the body. Drug metabolites are incorporated as part of the hair. If the rate of hair growth is known (or can be estimated), NAA could be used to detect drug metabolites in the hair, and the distance the metabolites are located above the follicle could determine how long ago the person had taken in the drugs.

43.   According to our textbook, polonium-210 has a half-life of 138 days. If the skeletal remains have undergone 5.25 half-lives, the skeleton is 5.25 × 138 days = 724.5 days (approximately 2 years).

45.   By using their lips to keep a fine point on their paint brushes, the young women at Westclox were ingesting small amounts of radioactive radium. Madame Curie, on the other hand, was

merely exposing the exterior of her body to the radioactive emissions of the radium isotopes. As a result, the young women showed symptoms of radiation poisoning where Madame Curie did not. However, it is important to note that antique clocks are unlikely to be dangerous unless the radium paint is ingested.

47.   May 2 is 7 days after April 26. If the half-life of tellurium-132 is 3 days, then May 2 is 2.33 half-lives after April 26. Two half-lives would result in 25% of the original mass. 2.33 half-lives results in 20% of the original mass remaining in the plume.
$(1/2)^{2.33} = 0.20 = 20\%$

Chapter 13

Chemical Equilibrium and Poisons

1. According to our textbook, the term toxin usually refers to a naturally occurring poisonous substance produced by a living organism. A poison is defined as any compound that injures or harms a living organism.

3. "Alle Dinge sind Gift, und nichts ist ohne Gift. Allein die Dosis macht, dass ein Ding kein Gift ist."
   "All things are poison, and nothing is without poison. The dosage alone determines that a thing isn't poison." – Paracelsus (1493–1541)
   As our textbook explains, almost any substance can be lethal if enough is present. Even water, which is necessary for life, can cause death by drowning.

5. The toxicity of a compound is measured according to the lethal dose in 50% of the population of interest. The shorthand notation for this quantity is the LD_{50} for the compound.

7. Chronic poisoning is poisoning that has taken place over a long period of time. In most cases, a toxic substance has accumulated in the body over a long period of time so that the cumulative effect of the toxic substance causes poisoning after that amount of time.

9. The reverse reaction of a system can occur as long as product molecules collide with sufficient energy to overcome the activation barrier and the correct orientation to produce the reagents.

11. The rate of forward reaction decreases as a function of reactant time typically because the amount of reagent decreases as a function of time.

13. It appears that a reaction has stopped when it reaches equilibrium because there is no net change in concentration of reactants or products with time. In fact, there is still conversion of reactant to product and product to reactant, but the rate of forward reaction is equal to the rate of reverse reaction.

15. A catalyst has no effect on the equilibrium constant, or the concentrations of the reactants or products at equilibrium. It simply speeds up the initial rates of the forward reactions allowing it to reach equilibrium more quickly.

17. If an equilibrium system for the reaction $A + B \rightarrow C + D$ had a very large equilibrium constant, the reaction mixture would contain mostly C and D when the system reached equilibrium.

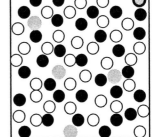

○A ◉B ○C ●D

19. The K number will tell you if it favors the right side of the arrow (large K value) or the left side of the arrow (small K value).

21. $CdX_2 = Cd^{2+} + 2\ X^-$; $K_{sp} = [Cd^{2+}][X^-]^2 = (x)(2x)^2 = 4x^3$; $x = \sqrt[3]{K_{sp}/4}$
    $CdY = Cd^{2+} + Y^{2-}$; $K_{sp} = [Cd^{2+}][Y^{2-}] = (x)(x) = x^2$; $x = \sqrt{K_{sp}}$
    (a) 1.2×10^{-5} M Cd^{2+}
    (b) 3.2×10^{-14} M Cd^{2+}
    (c) 1.0×10^{-6} M Cd^{2+}
    (d) 0.12 M Cd^{2+}
    Therefore, solution (d) has the greatest concentration of Cd^{2+} ion in solution.

23. All solutions listed contain weak monoprotic acids. The acid with the largest acid dissociation constant, K_a, will have the highest $[H^+]$ and the lowest pH.
    (c) $HCHO_2(aq)$, $K_a = 1.8\times10^{-4}$ will have the highest $[H^+]$ (lowest pH)

25. The four stresses and the response of the system are: (i) Add reactant: produce more product. (ii) Remove reactant: produce more reactant. (iii) Add product: produce more reactant. (iv) Remove product: produce more product.

27. Oxyhemoglobin (HbO_2) is transported to the cells in the blood. Once it arrives there, the oxygen is released by the oxyhemoglobin to produce hemoglobin (Hb), which is then circulated back to the lungs to gather more oxygen. In terms of Le Chatelier's principle, consider the equilibrium: $Hb + O_2 \rightleftharpoons HbO_2$. As blood leaving the lungs passes through the body's tissues, the concentration of O_2 dissolved in the blood decreases. The equilibrium must therefore shift to the left, and additional O_2 is released.

29. Carbon monoxide binds to hemoglobin more strongly than does oxygen. This competitive binding makes carbon monoxide toxic, as it prevents the delivery of oxygen to cells.

31. (a) H_2CO_3 concentration will increase and HCO_3^- concentration will decrease
    (b) H_2CO_3 concentration will decrease and HCO_3^- concentration will increase
    (c) H^+ concentration will increase and HCO_3^- concentration will increase
    (d) H_2CO_3 concentration will increase and H^+ concentration will decrease

33. Adding a sulfide such as Na_2S to solution would cause the solubility equilibrium to shift toward production of more solid, minimizing the amount of dissolved arsenic.

35. $PbF_2(s) = Pb^{2+}(aq) + 2\ F^-(aq)$
    $K_{sp} = [Pb^{2+}][F^-]^2 = 0.0043 \times (0.0022)^2$
    $K_{sp} = 2.1\times10^{-8}$

37. (a) $[F^-] = \sqrt{K_{sp}/[Pb^{2+}]} = \sqrt{2.1 \times 10^{-8}/0.0017} = 0.0035$ M
    (b) $[Pb^{2+}] = K_{sp}/[F^-]^2 = 2.1\times10^{-8} / 0.0012^2 = 0.015$ M
    (c) $[F^-] = \sqrt{K_{sp}/[Pb^{2+}]} = \sqrt{2.1 \times 10^{-8}/0.031} = 8.2\times10^{-4}$ M
    (d) $[Pb^{2+}] = K_{sp}/[F^-]^2 = 2.1\times10^{-8} / 0.079^2 = 3.4\times10^{-6}$ M

39. Causes: excess CO_2 levels create an excess acid state. This is usually due to a decrease in breathing, but can also be due to prolonged exercise, hypoglycemia, or severe dehydration.

41.   Dimercaprol binds to mercury, making it unable to cause its toxic effects in the body (which require the mercury(II) to be a free ion in solution). This is due to the extremely large binding constant between the mercury(II) ion with the –SH group of the cysteine.

43.   The alcohol in your blood is in equilibrium with the alcohol in air in your lungs. The more alcohol in the blood, the more alcohol in the air in your lungs. This is a direct application of equilibrium principles: the ratio of alcohol in the blood to alcohol in the air in your lungs remains constant.

45.   Arsenic poisoning is an example of chronic poisoning. The danger level is more substantial for an infant drinking formula prepared using contaminated water than an adult drinking the same water because the amount of arsenic present is more substantial in relation to the infant's mass than it is in relation to the mass of an adult drinking the same water.

47.   Cyanide poisoning can be "cured" by administering amyl nitrite ampoules that are broken onto a gauze pad and held under the nose. This process should be repeated 30 seconds every minute for 3 minutes and then sodium nitrite infused intravenously, and then finally sodium thiosulfate infused intravenously. Exposure to the nitrites converts a portion of hemoglobin to methemoglobin. Cyanide binds more strongly to methemoglobin than it does to cytochrome C oxidase. Sodium thiosulfate converts the cyanomethemoglobin to hemoglobin, thiocyanate, and sulfite. This allows the cyanide to be removed from the body as thiocyanate.

Chapter 14

Introduction to Biochemistry and DNA Analysis

1. Lipid molecules include a variety of compounds such as oils, fats, and waxes. Their shared physical property is that they are not soluble in water but are soluble in a nonpolar solvent.

3. According to our textbook, waxes are made by combining a fatty acid (a long carbon chain carboxylic acid molecule) and a long chain alcohol to form an ester. Both waxes and fatty acids are long chain carboxylic compounds, but the waxes are esters and the fatty acids are carboxylic acids.

5. Fats and oils are both examples of triglycerides. The difference between them is that fats are semi-solids at room temperature and oils are liquids at room temperature.

7. A fatty acid with a 24-carbon chain that is completely saturated is most likely a solid at room temperature. Stearic acid (an 18-carbon chain that is completely saturated) melts at 69°C, so it is a solid at room temperature. Arachidonic acid (a 20-carbon chain that is completely saturated) melts at 77°C, so it is also a solid at room temperature. As the chain length gets longer, the melting point increases, so it is reasonable to assume that a 24-carbon chain that is completely saturated will also be a solid at room temperature.

9. Starch is a polysaccharide of glucose. That means the starch is the polymer and glucose is the monomer. Cellulose is also a polysaccharide of glucose. That means that cellulose is the polymer and glucose is the monomer.

11. Cellulose:

Starch:

13. Amino acids contain an amino functional group, a carboxylic acid functional group, and an organic group (commonly called the sidechain) bonded to the middle carbon atom that distinguishes one amino acid from another.

15. The primary structure of a protein is the polypeptide chain that links amino acid monomer units. The secondary structure is how the amino acid chains interact with each other to fold into various superstructures.

17. Secondary structures are held together through hydrogen bonding and disulfide bonds.

19. Tertiary and quaternary structures of proteins are held together by hydrophobic interactions, ionic bridges, disulfide bonds, and hydrogen bonds.

21. Strands of DNA are held together through hydrogen bonding of the DNA base pairs. Covalent bonding between strands would be problematic because DNA replication and other functions require the "unzipping" of the DNA strands, and covalent bonds would not allow this.

23. The complementary strand to [GACTTAGGG] is [CTGAATCCC]. This is three codons.

25. The   complementary   strand   to   CCGTGGTTGCTTGGGCCCGGCG]   is [GGCACCAACGAACCCGGCCGC].

27. [CACCCCCGCGCGCACAAAAAC] codes for [His-Pro-Arg-Arg-His-Lys-Asn].

29. [GAAAAACCCCAAAACAACACC] codes for [Glu-Lys-Pro-Gln-Asn-Asn-Thr].

31. [Glu-Arg-Pro-His-Gly-Asp-Thr] is produced by [GAACGCCCCCACGGCGACACC].

33. [Thr-Pro-Pro-Asn-Asp-Gln-Gln] is produced by [ACCCCCCCCAACGACCAACAA].

35. mtDNA (mitochondrial DNA) comes only from the maternal side of the family. This can be a disadvantage because it makes it impossible to distinguish between relatives on the mother's side of the family. mtDNA does not decompose as easily as nuclear DNA, and there are multiple copies of mtDNA within a single cell, making recovery of a usable sample very simple.

37. All fibers can potentially be useful for investigative purposes. Perhaps an individual picked up a certain carpet fiber, a certain automobile fabric fiber, and a certain animal hair en route to a crime scene and deposited them there. Any one of those fibers might not be useful by itself, but the combination could establish beyond reasonable doubt that a certain suspect was present on the crime scene.

39. $0.00212 \times 0.00009 = 1.91 \times 10^{-7}$; $1 \div 1.91 \times 10^{-7} = 1$ in ~5,240,000 people

41. mtDNA can only be used to distinguish between two cousins if they are related through a brother and sister relationship (one cousin's father is the other cousin's sister). That way, they have different maternal lineage and will have different mtDNA.

43. According to our textbook, "even identical twins are believed to have slightly different DNA due to small variations and mutations that inevitably occur over time." However, this is not currently distinguishable using the techniques described in the chapter (at least no cases have been reported to my knowledge).

45. As hair grows, waste proteins are being excreted from the body. The primary structure of proteins contains peptide bonds, and the secondary structure involves hydrogen bonding and sulfide bonding between groups along the peptide chain. The interactions responsible for secondary structure are strong enough to trap trace amounts of arsenic or heavy metal poisons and retain some of those materials in the growing hair shaft.

47. If hair grows at a rate of 0.5 mm per day, then a 1.0 cm length (equivalent to 10. mm) represents 10. mm $\div$ 0.5 mm/day = 20 days of growth. If the first, fifth, and eighth samples tested positive for arsenic, then the victim had arsenic in his or her system between 0–20 days, 80–100 days, and 140–160 days prior to sample collection.